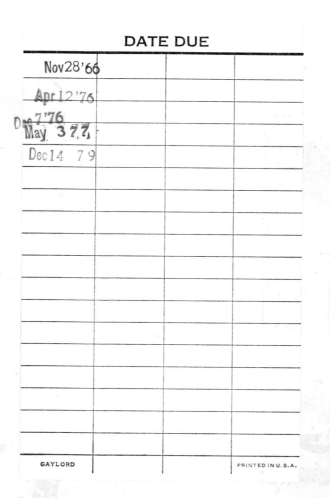

DATE DUE

Nov28'66			
Apr 12'76			
Dec 7'76			
May 3 77			
Dec 14 79			
GAYLORD			PRINTED IN U.S.A.

BIOLOGICAL MECHANISMS OF AGING

Publication Number 639
AMERICAN LECTURE SERIES®

A Monograph in
The BANNERSTONE DIVISION *of*
AMERICAN LECTURES IN LIVING CHEMISTRY

Edited by
I. NEWTON KUGELMASS, M.D., Ph.D., Sc.D.
Consultant to the Departments of Health and Hospitals
New York, New York

BIOLOGICAL MECHANISMS OF AGING

By

HOWARD J. CURTIS

Chairman of the Biology Department
Brookhaven National Laboratory
Upton, New York

CHARLES C THOMAS • PUBLISHER
Springfield • Illinois • U.S.A.

Published and Distributed Throughout the World by
CHARLES C THOMAS • PUBLISHER
BANNERSTONE HOUSE
301-327 East Lawrence Avenue, Springfield, Illinois, U.S.A.
NATCHEZ PLANTATION HOUSE
735 North Atlantic Boulevard, Fort Lauderdale, Florida, U.S.A.

With THOMAS BOOKS careful attention is given to all details of manufacturing and design. It is the Publisher's desire to present books that are satisfactory as to their physical qualities and artistic possibilities and appropriate for their particular use. THOMAS BOOKS will be true to those laws of quality that assure a good name and good will.

Printed in the United States of America
X-2

FOREWORD

O UR LIVING CHEMISTRY series was conceived by Editor and Publisher to advance the newer knowledge of chemical medicine in the cause of clinical practice. The interdependence of chemistry and medicine is so great that physicians are turning to chemistry, and chemists to medicine in order to understand the underlying basis of life processes in health and disease. Once chemical truths, proofs and convictions become sound foundations for clinical phenomena, key hybrid investigators clarify the bewildering panorama of biochemical progress for application in everyday practice, stimulation of experimental research, and extension of postgraduate instruction. Each of our monographs thus unravels the chemical mechanisms and clinical management of many diseases that have remained relatively static in the minds of medical men for three thousand years. Our new Series is charged with the *nisus élan* of chemical wisdom, supreme in choice of international authors, optimal in standards of chemical scholarship, provocative in imagination for experimental research, comprehensive in discussions of scientific medicine, and authoritative in chemical prespective of human disorders.

Dr. Curtis of Upton summarizes the biological mechanisms underlying the aging-process in all forms of life and synthesizes heterogeneous phenomena into sound foundations for modern gerontology. Body-time changes in the life cycle are surveyed from longitudinal studies with multidisciplinary technique and authoritative discrimination. The crystallized concepts not only give comprehensive understanding of the nature of life itself but of the inexhaustible potentialities of the living organism, of the immense complexity of the human constitution and of the individual velocity of aging. The first scientific experimenters in the field were Metchnikoff and Claude Bernard a century ago, following the ingenious clinicians Zerbi, Laennec, Floyer, Charcot and Bacon whose classical hypotheses on the time-keeping mechanisms of aging were tested by Loeb, Jennings, Carrel, Pearl, Comfort, Szilard and Burnet. Every living thing ages according to its species. The simplest organisms escape aging and death by dividing themselves into two new organisms. The embryo begins to age from the moment of fertilization, especially from mutations in somatic cells. Organs containing cells which seldom divide age with no opportunity to throw off spontaneous or induced mutations while organs containing cells that frequently undergo cell division barely participate in the aging process. Aging is either a progressive loss or function of deterioration in fixed post-mitotic cells; or a progressive accumulation or faulty copying in clonally dividing cells. Some cells such as epidermal cells which multiply throughout life gradually lose their vigor through repeated small injuries which may be mutational or immunological; while other cells such as the neurons gradually die out, several thousand daily and the inert materials of the body undergo biochemical changes.

Functional integration is the key to the stability of the internal environment during aging but the functions to be integrated are not the same. The kidney is only capable of maintaining internal stability in old age if the other organs age simultaneously. "Grow old along with me" is what the kidney says to the brain, heart, lungs, stomach and muscles for loss of functional reserve with aging enables the kidney to maintain internal stability only if all organs in the body age together. The functional disabilities of the organs are induced by changes in cell macromolecules and failure in DNA-RNA synthesis that disrupt enzyme formation. Progressive replacement of functional cells by connective tissue elements leads to homeostatic inefficiency with diminished protection from deleterious environmental influences. Aging thus involves reduction in the physiological activities of the cells, organs, tissues and body as a whole with corresponding decrease in adaptive reactions to environmental changes. The decrements in psychophysiological levels are balanced by increments in personality maturation, hence the years should pass unnoticed if all functions keep in step. Structural changes are continuous but only perceptible with time with accumulations of fat in the tissues, cholesterol in the arteries, chalk in the cartilages, stress effects in the vertebral bodies, metabolic alterations with abuses. Involutions like presbyopia are demonstrable in larval stages during the twenties; gout during the forties; and other disorders arrested or compensated beyond maturity. The body is a walking arena of conflict among organs deteriorating at different rates. The brain atrophies to almost half the size in old age, the leptomeninges thicken; the lungs lose elasticity, the bones strength; the kidneys show involution of parenchymal cells and replacement of connective tissue.

Each species has its characteristic life span, hence the link between somatic mutations and longevity ranging from an hour to a century. Why does the May fly have but two hours of amorous pursuit while the tortoise lives for two centuries? Why are three hundred years allowed a pike and only thirty years to Byron and Mozart? "The things of God knoweth no man." By some inexorable law, Nature has allotted to man a life span of one hundred and twenty years with flowering and fading but very few lives complete this span. The level of well-being, the pattern of aging and the duration of life are under genetic influence. The period of growth and development reaches a zenith maintained for a relatively short period of time soon followed by regressive changes. The gradual but variable decline in the degree of order maintained in the highly ordered physio-chemical systems of the body is the entropic basis of aging which gradually approaches the critical level of orderliness that delimits survival. In one view, there is no inherent process which pre-destines the demise; in the other, there is a specific cellular property that controls the rate and extent of aging unto exitus. Aging proceeds spontaneously even under the most ideal conditions without provocative agents. "Wherever there is life, there is an open ledger in which time makes an entry." But slow-consuming age is not all decay; it is the ripening, the swelling of the fresh life within, that withers and bursts the husk.

Life is like the "flame of a candle" whose form is constant

while each particle changes every moment unto extinction. Death takes small bites in aging but when death comes, it destroys structures still capable of living and destroyed by others, more degenerate. Heterchromism of the organs shortens life. Reparative ability as an expression of cellular vitality weakens with age according to exponential law, diminishing very rapidly at the beginning of life and diminishing gradually thereafter. Plasma is the means of interaction between organs and the site of an organic memory for every previous physiological state has left some modifying impression there. Our present state is inseparable from our past for we think with only a part of our past but it is with our entire past that we desire, will and act. Man is most likely to endure by becoming more and more individualized; freedom to think and act as an individual is still one of the best ways of decreasing the rate of aging. The study of aging is coming down from the clouds of nebulous speculation to the laboratories of experimental science. Once the underlying mechanisms of aging are revealed and come within the reach of our tools, man may indeed become the master of his corporal fate. The practice of what can only be called molecular surgery might give us new organs for old, may suppress deleterious genes from our seed, and enhance our creative and longevity capacity. Who can set bounds to human ingenuity? We await the unveiling of one of those heartless secrets which are called the Laws of Nature. The adverse consequences of aging can and will be deferred with the gradual increase in the useful life span among the most visible of people surviving in an age that finds their minds and bodies superfluous.

"Corporis et fortunae bonorum ut initium finis est.
Omnia orta occidunt, et orta senescunt."

I. NEWTON KUGELMASS, M.D., PH.D., SC.D., *Editor*

PREFACE

THE SCIENCE OF GERONTOLOGY is rapidly emerging as a respected branch of learning. It is difficult to understand why it has lagged so far behind the other sciences, since interest in staving off the inevitable ravages of time has been apparent for centuries. The difficulty, perhaps, has been the failure to recognize the biological phenomenon of aging apart from the various diseases by which it manifests itself. Biological scientists have understandably been so engrossed in trying to solve such problems as cancer and heart disease, that they have given little attention to the degenerative process which creates the fertile ground for these diseases to grow on.

During the past ten years there has been a remarkable development in biology which has seen our older concepts outmoded, and new ones introduced which no one dreamed of even a few years ago. It has been exciting to observe and to take some part in the development of gerontology during this period.

It is presumptive of me to try to formulate the current ideas in the field into a comprehensive theory of aging in terms of basic biological reactions. But it has become apparent to me that what the field sorely needs is a framework on which to build the science. Such a formulation exists, for example, for genetics, and this science has made enormous strides because of it. It is my hope that this monograph might be one of the beginnings of a framework for gerontology. For this reason I have many times reached well beyond the proven facts to speculate on the way things might be to fit a coherent theory. If ten years from now these ideas remain intact, I shall be surprised. I will be acutely disappointed if this formulation does not materially assist in building a better structure.

For those who are looking for hints on how to prolong life, I am afraid the book will be a disappointment. There is no doubt whatever but that such studies as those reported here will eventually lead to a prolongation of the human life span, but how they will do so is not now apparent. In the meantime, a great deal is being done to ward off the degenerative diseases and to turn the later years of life into happy and fruitful ones, but that important phase of gerontology has not been covered here.

The book is written for professional people, but intelligent laymen interested in the subject should be able to read it with little trouble.

It is a pleasure to acknowledge the assistance of my colleagues, Mrs. Katherine Stevenson, Miss Catharine Crowley, Mr. John Tilley and Dr. John Berech, who have performed much of the experimental work reported here, and Mrs. Edna Hodges who has assisted in the preparation of the manuscript.

HOWARD J. CURTIS

CONTENTS

BIOLOGICAL MECHANISMS OF AGING

Chapter 1

INTRODUCTION

A S THE human population of the world has become increasingly independent of its environment, and has learned to conquer a great many diseases, the average human life span has increased remarkably. It was a relatively few years ago in our western civilization, and is still true today in many parts of the world, that the life expectancy extended only a few years beyond youth, and a sexagenarian was a rarity. As more and more diseases have been conquered and as the standard of living has increased, the average life expectancy has progressively increased. The populations of western countries are growing older and older. This has spurred interest in the problems of senescence, and at the same time accelerated inquiry into the causes of aging.

The phenomenon of aging is one with which everyone is familiar. All of us have known from childhood that we will undergo adverse changes with time which will eventually lead to death from some cause. We have accepted this as inevitable. It so coincides with our everyday experience that relatively few people have even bothered to ask why. Yet those who have asked why have had to content themselves with very vague explanations.

Aging is thus one of the most universal of biological phenomena, and yet until the past few years the basic mechanism involved in this process has been almost completely unknown. We are finally getting some insight into this biological phenomenon, and it is the purpose of this monograph to examine the state of our present knowledge, the validity of the various theories, and the way in which these ideas apply to the specific problems encountered in the various branches of biology.

3

THE NATURE OF AGING

The term aging is itself misleading. There is no doubt that all plants and animals grow from a single cell and go through a more or less complex series of changes with time. In the human we are all familiar with the sequence of birth, rapid growth, puberty, adulthood, old age, and finally death. This is the total pattern of aging, so it can correctly be stated that a person starts to age immediately following conception. The aspect of aging with which we will be concerned here is the degenerative process which starts in adulthood and continues its inevitable course to death. This process is known as senescence.

A mammalian organism is extremely complex, and the subtle changes responsible for senescence must be equally complex. There is little wonder then that theories have been vague, and even a precise definition of senescence cannot be agreed upon by gerontologists.

Senescence is certainly not merely something which leads to death, for acceptance of this idea would lead to such absurd

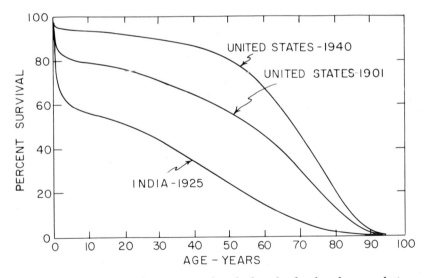

Figure 1. Percentage of survivors of male live births for the populations indicated (modified from Comfort, 1964.)

conclusions as, automobiles cause senscence because they decrease life expectancy in this country. The various communicable diseases and even cancer might be put in this same category since one might consider that they are accidents.

However, a look at the survival curves for various populations (Fig. 1), will show that death is not merely a chance phenomenon in the human. For example, the aging of laboratory glassware (following Comfort, 1964) takes place by chance breakage. A group of 100 beakers will "age" according to an exponential curve as shown in Figure 2. Clearly human populations, and indeed all populations of biological objects, age according to quite a different curve. This must mean then, that death in a living organism is not a phenomenon which has as great a probability of occurring at all ages, but the probability of death becomes greater and greater as time goes on. Thus one way to think of aging is that it is a deteriorative process which renders the organism more susceptible to disease, or less well able to

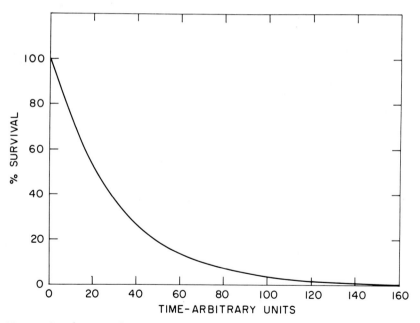

Figure 2. Theoretical survival curve showing the type of curve which would obtain if death were due entirely to chance.

withstand stress. In mammals there is no such thing as "dying of old age." There is always a specific cause of death and all are responsible for death in quite young individuals. However, the probability of contracting and succumbing to these diseases increases logarithmically, and for man in the United States in 1960 the death rate at any age doubles about every eight years. At age fifty there is about a 1 per cent probability of dying during the following year, but at age fifty-eight this probability has doubled. Another aspect of Figure 1 shows the same thing in a different way. Modern civilization, which includes plenty of good food and excellent medical care, has increased the life expectancy of most Americans in a truly phenomenal way. Death from all causes has steadily decreased for all age groups over the past century. The average American now lives almost twice as long as he did a century ago and his life expectancy is still increasing. However, Figure 1 shows that the maximum life span has not changed in modern times and, as far as we know, has never changed.

As one examines the actuarial data it is seen that the gains in longevity over the past century have been almost entirely in the younger age groups, and the truly spectacular gains have been made in infant mortality. We are a very long way from the times when parents did not bother to name an infant until he had survived smallpox, but as one examines the older groups, it is found that the fifty-year-old group has a smaller probability of death per year than the same group a century ago—but not much smaller. Considering the eighty-year-old groups, the probability of death per year is about the same now as it was a century ago. This is shown in Figure 3 which plots the death rate for a very stable population, that of Sweden, which has benefited fully from modern medicine. The graph shows the mortality rates for two different generations. One can see how dramatically the death rate has decreased in about half a century for young adults, but how it has changed hardly at all in the very old groups.

Apparently when the body reaches a certain state, deterioration provides such a fertile field for disease that if one disease is

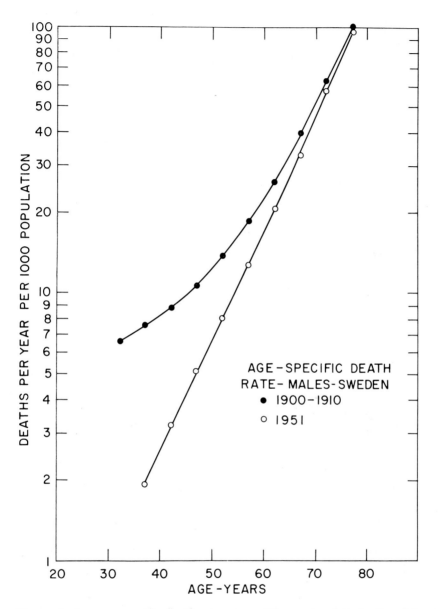

Figure 3. Log age-specific death rate *vs* age (Gompertz plot) for Swedish males before and after the advent of modern medicine. This shows the striking decrease in death rate for young men, but the lack of change for old men (data from Jones, 1960).

avoided, another is sure to strike soon. Dublin (1949) has estimated that if it were possible to eliminate all cardiovascular and kidney diseases, it would only add 7.5 years to the average human life span in this country. If all cancer were conquered, it would add only 1.5 years. There is not much more to be gained from the cure of the communicable diseases. Mice that are kept in a completely germ-free environment do not live any longer than similar animals raised under reasonably sanitary conditions. This is a rather discouraging outlook, and shows that a completely new approach is necessary if the human life span is to be extended appreciably. For this, it will first be necessary to understand senescence and the factors which are responsible for its development. When this is achieved, it may be possible to develop some methods for slowing its progress.

It would seem that modern medicine has been able to do very little for old people, and this is true if one is considering only mortality figures. If one considers the health, happiness and general well-being of older people, the statement is probably incorrect although this is difficult to document. One certainly gets the impression that old people now are living happier and more productive lives than in the past because medical science keeps them healthier and modern civilization is learning more about the problems of older persons and how to deal with them. This is the science of geriatrics and as our population is growing older the science is becoming increasingly important. However, the problem of senescence remains largely untouched and this is the basic biological problem which will be considered in this monograph.

THE FORCE OF MORTALITY

As has been indicated, the only definite end point of senescence is death. Yet we know that the organism is becoming more and more susceptible to disease for a long time prior to the actual event. It would be satisfying if there were a measure of this susceptibility, or an index one could apply to a population which would express the degree of senescence.

In 1825, Gompertz, in studying mortality tables, noticed that if for any population he plotted the log of the mortality rate at any age against the age, he obtained a straight line relationship for ages beyond puberty. This plot has been extensively used since that time and is known as the Gompertz plot. One such plot is shown in Figure 3. It shows how the death rate increases rapidly with age to the point where the probability of death becomes so large it is a virtual certainty. The death rate at any age can then be taken as a measure of the stability of the population at that age, or a measure of the force of mortality. This has been widely accepted as a measure of senescence. In Figure 1, one can say that the people of India are more senescent at age fifty than are the people of the United States. However, this statement has very little real value as far as the basic concepts of senescence are concerned. There is every indication that a population of Indians living under the same standards of nutrition, sanitation, and medical care as exist in the United States would live about as long. Nevertheless the Gompertz plot is the best way of expressing the trend of the mortality of a population and the way it may change. It is widely used as such.

SENESCENCE IN LOWER FORMS

This discussion has been centered largely on mammals and especially on man. Undoubtedly, aging is a universal biological phenomenon and there is a persistent tendency on the part of writers on the subject to treat aging as something identical in all organisms. People tend to think of senescence in a tree, a bacterium, an annual plant, and a man as being basically the same phenomenon, differing only in its expression. I believe this approach to be fallicious and to lead to unnecessary complications. Each of these four biological entities represents a different kind of aging. It will be well at this point to discuss each briefly and to take them up in more detail as the various theories of aging are discussed.

A suspension of bacteria is, as far as we know, immortal. As long as the suspending medium is kept somewhere near optimal, cell division will continue indefinitely and the size of the suspension will be limited only by the size of the vessel available. If one focuses attention on a single cell, it will undergo division, the daughter cells will each undergo division, and so on. Whether or not the individual cell ages is thus an academic question. If conditions are adverse, individual cells and even the entire culture will die, but one could hardly call this senescence in the same way in which one speaks of senescence in man.

The second type is the annual plant which grows, reproduces, ages, and dies according to a definite pattern. This can be called genetically programmed aging. The plant does not gradually deteriorate and finally succumb to some disease or accident. The normal physiological processes of the plant cause it to dry up and die. One can, by various devices such as the regulation of the day length, moisture content, and nutrient of the soil, etc., alter the time of occurrence of the various phases of development in the plant and thus in a sense alter the aging by as much as a factor of two or more. This does not alter the fact that the program exists and is being carried forward.

The aging of a tree represents still another type of aging. If it is deciduous it loses its leaves regularly according to the genetic program, but this is certainly not senescence. The tree keeps growing at about the same rate until it gets into mechanical difficulties. The sap cannot be transported to the topmost branches, and the lower branches cannot grow out far enough to receive the proper light. The tree thus deteriorates and dies, but it is basically as good as it ever was. A twig taken from an ancient tree can be rooted to produce a perfect new tree, and seed taken from the giant sequoias of California which are 3,000 years old is as good as seed taken from a young tree. Here again "aging" in this case is clearly quite different from that of the other cases, and indeed each is so different from the other that they should all be referred to by different names.

This by no means exhausts the different kinds of aging and senescence which have been described for different kinds of plants or animals, but it will suffice for the present. Certainly some of the features of one type of aging are present in other types, but a search for a common denominator for all types has so far been unsuccessful. Part of the confusion which has permeated the problem of aging in the past has been due to the effort to find "the cause" of senescence. For each theory that has been advanced, it is possible to point to many exceptions to it in nature.

The present treatment will abandon this approach and try to explain separately the different phenomena of aging in different biological systems in terms of modern biological concepts. Man is certainly most interested in himself and indeed knows more about himself than about any other biological system. It is thus natural to approach the problem of senescence first by trying to understand it in the mammal and then turning to other forms in an effort to explain the phenomenon there, and to use phenomena observed in one system to explain those in others.

THE GENETIC BASIS OF AGING

It has been truly said that the way to attain a very old age is to select grandparents who lived to a very old age. Thus the genetic component of aging is too well established to need further elucidation. It forms a very useful tool for research in aging in that there are some strains of mice which live quite long lives and others quite short lives; and indeed for apparently normal mice there can be a difference of as much as a factor of three in the median life spans of various strains of mice. An examination of the characteristics of these different strains has led to some interesting results as will be discussed later. However, one must examine such data very carefully because many strains have built-in genetic weaknesses. For example, mice of strain C58 as developed by McDowell will succumb to leukemia at about age nine months in 100 per cent of the animals. It is difficult to think of these mice as aging about four times as fast as mice who have a median life span of thirty-six months. Mice such as the C58 strain having a very pronounced weak-link would certainly never exist for long in the wild state. The process of natural selection would gradually weed out such animals, leaving animals having many different causes of natural death. In selecting a strain of mice for experimentation it is important to choose one having a variety of causes of death.

This same phenomenon occurs in humans, in which mutations occur which predispose an individual to the development of a particular disease. Since modern society tends to prevent the process of natural selection from operating in such cases, there is the very real possibility that such genetic defects may gradually build up in the human population to reach alarming proportions. This is getting to be an important part of the practice of medicine, as evidenced by the fact that many modern medical schools now have departments of genetics.

There is another aspect of the genetic problem which deserves comment. A mouse completes his life span in about one-thirtieth the time as does a man, or one may say that aging in a mouse is thirty times faster than it is in a man. One can easily say that this is because a mouse has a genetic constitution such that his life span is about two years, but this does not answer the question. Is it legitimate to say that in a mouse senescence develops thirty times faster? I believe not. Each plant or animal is endowed by his genetic background with a potential for a certain kind of life and life span. There is a specific genetic program which is determined by the particular set of genes which the plant or animal has inherited. In general, mice have a genetic program which takes about two years for completion, while man requires about seventy years. This program is accurately followed and for the human can be accurately predicted. The stages of rapid growth, puberty, etc., finally leading to old age are well known and it would seem unwise to attribute one part of the program, senescence, to "unnatural" or pathological causes, still maintaining that the other parts such as puberty are natural and physiological.

At first one might think this a very fatalistic approach to the problem of senescence. However, it need not be. We now have it within our abilities to alter the genetic program of a number of plants and animals. As already indicated, the genetic program of annual plants can be altered easily, and puberty in a mammal can be either advanced or retarded. It does not seem out of the question to think of altering senescence, which is the final phase of the program.

In order to alter senescence it is first necessary to understand it, just as one must have a thorough understanding of endocrine physiology before one can successfully alter the onset of puberty. The purpose of this monograph is to outline our present knowledge of the subject, and to indicate promising areas of attack on the problem.

METHODS OF STUDYING SENESCENCE

It will be recognized at once from the foregoing that aging is a complex phenomenon involving all disciplines of biology. It is apparent that the older approaches such as pathology, physiology, etc., have made extremely important contributions to the problem by giving us the descriptive framework on which any theories of senescence must be built. More modern concepts of genetics and molecular biology are being brought to bear on the mechanisms of senescence, and through these and other modern approaches considerable progress is being made.

If one wishes to undertake longevity experiments with laboratory animals, one is practically limited to the rat and mouse, and even then one is forced to wait two to three years for the answer to one experiment. Many types of physiological experiments are very difficult to perform on small rodents, so, many of these are performed on human populations, and this greatly curtails the types of experimentation. Many actuarial studies have been undertaken on human populations and these have yielded valuable guidelines for our thinking concerning problems of senescence.

As already mentioned, aging and senescence may be quite different phenomena in mammals than in lower forms. However, many facets of the problem are doubtlessly common to all forms and some of these can best be studied in one form of life, and some in another. Many phenomena relative to cellular aging can best be studied in bacteria. Other problems relative to genetic considerations can best be studied in *Drosophila*, etc. Each specific problem of aging finds some living form in which

it can best be studied. The application of results on lower forms
to problems of human senescence is not always easy, but nevertheless such results are being welded together to form a coherent,
if somewhat complex, picture of the mechanisms of senescence.

Chapter 2

THEORIES OF AGING

T HROUGH THE YEARS there have been many theories advanced to account for the phenomenon of senescence, but it has only been in recent years that serious attempts have been made to understand it. Prior to a half century ago there was only a very elementary understanding of the scientific basis of biology, so exact theories could not be formulated. Prior to that time it seemed quite natural to think of things wearing out, and apparently few people gave the matter serious thought, except in vain attempts to empirically discover an elixir which would prolong human life.

In this chapter some of the ideas and theories concerning the mechanisms of senescence will be briefly reviewed. The more promising of these will then be dealt with in subsequent chapters.

THE WEAR AND TEAR THEORY

It is perhaps natural that the first of the modern theories of aging should emphasize the "wearing out" idea. This was most forcefully put forward by Pearl (1924) in his "rate of living" theory or as others have expressed it, the "wear and tear" theory. As the name implies, the theory postulates that the organism wears out with use much like inanimate objects. A more modern version of the idea states that as the cells of the organism differentiate to form the adult organism, they are endowed with certain amounts of vital substances; essential enzymes for example. As these substances are used up, and cannot be replaced, the cells become inefficient and death of the organism soon follows.

As a concept this theory seems easy to accept and a great deal

15

of quite convincing evidence can be brought to bear to support it. On the other hand, there is also much to argue against the concept, and in general, its many advocates have failed to produce the evidence necessary for its acceptance. It would seem, however, that there must be at least something to the idea, even though it may not be the most important part of the problem. Future theories must take this evidence into account and incorporate these ideas into their fabric. For these reasons this evidence will be extensively discussed in a subsequent chapter.

MATHEMATICAL THEORIES

There have been many so-called mathematical theories of aging in which an equation is formulated to fit an empirical mortality curve. The first of these was formulated by Gompertz in 1825 who plotted the log of the death rate for different populations as a function of age and noted that the death rate, or probability of death at any age (the age-specific death rate), increases rapidly as the population ages. This indicates that death cannot be a purely chance affair, but that people become increasingly unable to withstand the stress of their environment as they age. The age-specific death rate has often been taken as a measure of the physiological age (as opposed to chrono-logical age) of a population. Anything which changes the death rate at any age thus changes the physiological age of the population.

A number of investigators have developed equations to fit the death rate curves on the basis of various hypotheses. The assumptions have been rather vague and the equations which have been developed have enough constants so the many death rate curves can be fitted reasonably well. They have thus failed to produce a biological concept about aging which can be used for constructive planning of research. The various equations have been recently extensively reviewed by Strehler (1962).

THE CELLULAR INTERACTION THEORY

In an organism as complex as a mammal, almost every part of the body is dependent on the proper functioning of every other part. Thus the pancreas is dependent on the proper functioning of the liver, and vice versa. There is also a good deal of evidence to suggest that an individual cell in an organ is dependent on, or at least influenced by, the neighboring cells of that organ. If the skin is damaged, the cells next to the damaged part immediately undergo proliferation. The blood capillaries also start to grow into the regenerating region. When the organ has reached its proper size, the proliferation stops and normality is restored.

There is at least some evidence that this process is under humoral control. Rats can be joined together in parabiosis so the blood mixes. Bucher (1963) found in such animals that if the liver is partially removed in one animal, not only is there a rapid proliferation of the damaged liver, but the liver of the parabiotic twin also undergoes proliferation. This indicates that in the normal liver the cells are continually producing a compound which enters the blood stream and is specific for the inhibition of cell division of liver cells. If for any reason the number of cells is reduced, the concentration of this substance falls, allowing cellular proliferation to take place until the increased numbers of cells bring the concentration of the inhibitory substance back to normal. Thus a feed-back mechanism exists for the maintenance of the proper size of the liver. If something should interfere with this mechanism, or the cells fail to respond to it in the proper way, then neoplasia could occur on the one hand, or organ degeneration on the other.

This is only one example of the countless number of feed-back mechanisms which must exist in a mammal. These are even known to act within the cell. Leavitt and Umbarger (1962) have shown that the synthesis of leucine within the bacterial cell is controlled by such a system acting on the DNA of the cell. Thus the organism is a delicate balance of a multitude of forces acting to maintain the individual in proper working order, or homeostasis. This is what distinguishes a living organism from a machine, although it must be admitted that some modern electronic equipment is "almost human" in its operation.

In such a complex system the possibilities for malfunction

seem almost infinite. One can easily imagine that in a very
young organism all systems start out working perfectly, with a
perfect interrelationship with all other parts. If the rate constants of all the reactions are not perfectly coordinated, the whole
process may finally get out of synchrony and degenerate. It is
as if in an orchestra there was no leader, and each member had
to depend upon his own sense of timing, which was good, but
not perfect. When this orchestra played a number, it would
sound fine for a while, but in time the small errors in rhythm
would make themselves felt, and before long there would be
merely a jumble of uncoordinated sound.

This theory is difficult to formulate in definite terms, and
even more difficult to bring to bear direct evidence supporting
it. This does not prove that it is, at least in part, not correct.
Certainly one of the well known concomitants of senescence,
cancer, can be explained by a mechanism such as this (Failla,
1958), and if cancer can be, then certainly organ degeneration
should also be explicable in these terms. This much can be said
with some assurance: Any change which affects any of the
feed-back mechanisms of the body, although apparently unre-
lated to the initial causitive event, may lead to senescence
through a complex series of reactions.

Very little more can be said about this concept at the present
time, but it should not be discarded. In the complex series of
events which comprise the phenomenon of senescence, it seems
probable that the intricate interactions between cells will play
a part, but just what part and how important it is will have to
be determined by future research.

THE COLLAGEN THEORY

This concept postulates that collagen, a fibrous protein, is
formed in various tissues at a relatively slow rate and is eliminated very slowly if at all. Further, the fibers tend to shrink
with time and "choke-off" the tissues of which they are a part.
The process so hampers the function of the tissues that they
become very inefficient and death ensues.

The idea is very old—a century ago Bogomolitz vigorously

espoused this theory and had his patients taking medicine designed to dissolve the collagen. None of his concoctions produced any effect either on the collagen or on the longevity of the patients. Nevertheless, many gerontologists today feel that this represents at least a strong contributing factor in the aging process.

This idea has been strengthened considerably by the work of Vertzar (1957) who showed that collagen will shrink when placed in warm water by a very exact amount. Collagen from a young animal will shrink more than that from an old one, and for any species of animal the age can be judged by the heat shrinkage of the collagen. This difference is due to a change in the cross-linkage of the strands of fibrous protein, which apparently gradually form as time progresses. Thus not only does the amount of collagen increase, but its nature changes with age.

There is no doubt that these events occur. The old appearance of the skin of an elderly person is due largely to the accumulation and shrinkage of collagen. However, many organs, such as muscle, accumulate virtually no collagen and yet "age" as fast as any other organ. Also, many lower animals contain no collagen at all and yet exhibit all the signs of aging.

It appears that the known accumulation of collagen may contribute to some of the symptoms of old age, such as a wrinkled skin and a decreased rate of wound healing, but it is hard to think of this as a basic cause of aging.

THE WASTE PRODUCT THEORY

This idea, also, is quite old and still has its adherents. It postulates that some waste products of metabolism are not readily excreted either from the individual cells or from the intercellular fluids and thus pile up to slowly poison the organism or otherwise interfere with its function. The callogen theory is a special case of this theory.

Many years ago Carrell and Ebeling (1923) attempted to show that there were substances in the blood of older persons which inhibited growth and interferred with respiration and metabolism of cells. Many of the tissue culture techniques which he so successfully developed were designed to test these ideas. It is certainly true that embryonic tissue fluid will promote growth of tissue cultures and tissue fluid from adult animals will not. However, the difference is between very young and adult tissues, not between adult and senescent ones. It seems that Carrell failed to produce convincing evidence for his ideas.

Another variation of the waste product theory arises from the observation that, what appears to be waste products do indeed accumulate in some cells as a function of age (Strehler, *et al.* 1959). These substances, known as lipofuccins, may build up in heart muscle to become 30 per cent of the weight of the heart. In many nerve cells they may occupy a large fraction of the volume of the cytoplasm. They are apparently insoluble products of metabolism, and once formed remain in the cell for the remainder of its life. This is true, but the significance of this finding remains obscure. A great many tissues in old animals do not contain significant concentrations of these substances. Further, Sulkin and Srevanij (1960) have studied this phenomenon in rats and found they can produce these age pigments in nerve cells of young rats by various treatments such as hypoxia, vitamin E deficiency, and various chemical treatments. The age pigments remain for the rest of the lives of the rats, but they live a normal life-span and the pigments apparently do no harm. They found that laboratory animals do not develop lipofuccins nearly as rapidly as do wild animals, but the available evidence indicates that wild animals do not age as rapidly as laboratory animals. The present indication would seem to be that these pigments are a rather unimportant symptom of aging in certain cases and in certain tissues.

THE ENDOCRINE GLANDS

One of the most important concerns of mankind is his reproductive capacity, and undoubtedly as soon as man started living beyond about fifty years of age, a decline in this capacity was noted. It is not surprising then that the search for the fountain of youth would have a strong sexual component, and that the decline in sexual powers was considered both the symptom and the cause of senescence. Apparently the well-known fact that eunuchs live about as long as other men was overlooked. Less than a century ago, it was felt that a testicular transplant from a young man or monkey, if successful, would surely bring rejuvenation. Testicular extracts were much in vogue, and are probably still tried in many parts of the world.

As endocrine physiology was developed and especially as hormones were discovered and studied, interest in the subject freshened. Many hormone preparations were tried and the results were, of course, all negative. Gonodal hormones have no effect on the senescence of somatic cells. Indeed much the same can be said of the other hormones, although some, such as the growth hormone of the pituitary, may possibly be involved to a small extent in one way or another.

It was noted that the excretion of hormones, which apparently measures their rate of synthesis, declines steadily with age. Indeed the seventeen-ketosteroid excretion is so characteristic that it is thought by some to be a good measure of the physiological age of the individual, and this may be found to be true when one arrives at a definition of physiological age. It would seem that the decrease in gonodal hormones is a symptom rather than a cause of senescence.

As more is learned about endocrine physiology, the picture seems to get more and more complex. The pituitary gland is the master gland and seems to control the other endocrine glands through the secretion of a series of specific trophic hormones. It is, in turn, regulated partly by the central nervous system and partly by feed-back mechanisms from the other glands. In this way most of the bodily processes of growth, puberty, maturation, and perhaps senescence are regulated. It appears that the endocrine system, and especially the pituitary gland, are responsible for carrying out the genetically programmed growth and development of the mammal. It would then be natural to also assign this system major responsibility for senescence. One can think that the various endocrine glands "wear out" and slow down, thus causing the gradual deterioration of the whole animal.

However, the work of McGavarck (1951) would not bear out this concept. There are at least twenty-four different hormones secreted by the various glands. Some of these secretions seem to increase with age, some decrease, some are virtually unchanged throughout life, and some undergo rather wide fluctuations associated with specific developmental periods such as puberty. It is true that if one attempts to evoke a response from an endocrine gland, the response will be reduced in older animals. For example, if rats are suddenly placed in a cold environment, there will be an increased thyroid activity leading to an increased metabolism, and this response will be faster and larger in young rats than in old ones. However, the responses of all organ systems are faster and larger in young than in old animals, and there seems, if anything, to be less of a deficit in endocrine function with age than for any other part of the body.

For these reasons it seems doubtful that one can blame the endocrine system for the deterioration of senescence.

THE CALCIUM THEORY

Recently, Selye (1960) has put forward the idea that senescence is caused largely by a defect in calcium metabolism. When rats are given large doses of vitamin D or parathyroid hormone, calcium is laid down in many of the soft tissues in a manner somewhat resembling calcification in old age. Any site of injury or trauma under these conditions will result in a calcium deposit in that area which renders that tissue nonfunctional. There is a shift of calcium from the bones to the soft tissues. The bones get brittle, cataracts form, the skin becomes wrinkled, and in many other ways these rats resemble old rats. These results caused Selye to conclude that the calcium shift from bone to soft tissues is the cause of aging rather than its result, as has always been supposed.

However, it should be pointed out that the doses of vitamin or hormone used in these experiments were far in excess of anything which has been used therapeutically or which exists in the living animal. The symptoms observed in some respects superficially resemble the changes observed in senescence, but it is hard to think of this as a basic cause. For example, many normal animals become very senescent with no cataract formation and no calcification of the arteries or other organs. In general, the calcification seen in old animals is not nearly as severe as that seen in these rats. Finally, there is no evidence that even fairly large overdoses of vitamin D or parathyroid hormone will shorten the life expectancy of any animal. It appears that these are pathological studies of the consequences of overdoses of these drugs and probably bear little, if any, resemblance to the biological phenomenon of senescence.

THE SOMATIC MUTATION THEORY

Another theory which has received a good deal of attention recently is the somatic mutation theory. The idea behind this theory is quite old, but it has only recently been formulated in definite terms by Failla (1958), and Curtis and Gebhard (1958b), Szilard (1959) and others. According to this theory the somatic cells of the body develop spontaneous mutations in the same way as do the germ cells. Once a mutation has been formed, subsequent cell divisions will perpetuate it. As more and more cells develop mutations, the time comes when an appreciable fraction of the cells are mutated. Practically all mutations are deleterious, so the cells carrying mutations are less well able to perform their functions. The organs become inefficient and senescent. This has been a very attractive theory, but until very recently there has been virtually no evidence to either support or deny it.

AUTOIMMUNITY

One of the phenomena known to occur with aging is the development of autoimmune reactions (see Walford, 1962). Apparently, some of the cells of the body synthesize proteins which are immunologically different from the rest of the proteins of the body and thus lead to immune and anaphalactic reactions within the body. Several diseases which increase sharply with age, such as rheumatoid arthritis, are known to be caused by autoimmune reactions and a number of others are strongly suspected of being due to this cause. It is even thought by some that autoimmune reactions play a large part in cancer etiology. For these reasons autoimmunity is thought to be one of the causes of aging and this theory must be considered.

If, as postulated, cells manufacture proteins which are not quite identical to the original proteins in their immunological characteristics, the only reasonable assumption is that a mutation has occurred in some of the somatic cells. Thus this theory is really one of the consequences of the somatic mutation theory.

CIRCULATORY FAILURE

A common observation in mammals and especially in man, is that circulatory deficiency increases with age, and many people have felt that this condition is really the cause of aging in the mammal. Not only does the heart muscle become weaker, but the capillary circulation tends to break down, causing small areas of anoxia throughout the body. As a result, the organs themselves become inefficient and weak. Many individual cells die and are replaced by scar tissue (collagen) which tends to shrink in time and thereby choke off more capillaries causing more anoxia. There seems to be no doubt that this process occurs in the mammal, and that many of the symptoms of aging are due to this cause. It has often been suggested that this process is one which promotes carcinogenesis. However, this is something peculiar to the mammal, and could not be taken as a very universal theory of aging.

The reason for the capillary breakdown is not known, but certainly one of the best ideas is that the endothelial cells of the capillary walls undergo mutation which leads to the breakdown of that part of the capillary. These cells are known to undergo division from time to time, and cell failure by mutation is more probable with cell division. Further, it only takes failure of one cell to block a capillary. Again it appears that this theory is probably one facet of the somatic mutation theory.

SUMMARY

Many different theories have been put forward to account for senescence and most of them have been based on observations which have considerable validity. Some appear to be based on phenomena which are more nearly symptoms of aging than causes. Among these are the callogen, hormone, and waste product theories. Other theories such as mathematical theories and cellular interaction theories do not lead to constructive ideas for future progress. Certain portions of the wear and tear theory and the somatic mutation theory seem to hold excellent promise of explaining many of the phenomena of aging, and they suggest many experimental approaches to the problem. They will be discussed in detail in subsequent chapters.

Chapter 3

THE WEAR AND TEAR THEORY

T HIS THEORY was briefly mentioned in the last chapter, but because of its importance, both historically and conceptually, it merits a full discussion. Conceptually it has the advantage of being in accord with everyday experience. We are quite used to the idea of things wearing out, and the harder they are used the faster they wear out. The dire consequences of "burning the candle at both ends" has been well recognized for many centuries, although evidence bearing on this idea has been lacking until quite recently.

RATE OF LIVING THEORY

As mentioned earlier, Pearl (1928) was much impressed with the relation between energy expenditure and longevity. Earlier experiments by Loeb and Northrop (1917) showed conclusively that the longevity of *Drosophila* depended upon the temperature at which they were kept; the low temperatures slowing the metabolic rate (the rate of living) and extending the life span. Between 10° and 30° C there was nearly a ten-fold change in longevity. Pearl tried to discern from the temperature coefficient the basic chemical reaction involved in the aging process, but it appeared that the problem was too complex for resolution in this way. This relation between body temperature and longevity is, in general, true of all poikilothermic animals which have so far been tested.

It would be dangerous to extrapolate too far from these experiments. It appears that the genetic program of these animals has been changed by their environment, just as the longevity of a plant can be changed in a number of ways. What this may

26

have to do with senescence in the mammal, however, remains uncertain.

Pearl (1924) also made a number of studies on longevity in human populations in relation to rate of living. One of the most exhaustive of these was on various labor groups in England and Wales. He divided the subjects into two categories depending on whether they worked outdoors or indoors. For each one he classed the workers into five groups according to the degree of physical labor involved in their work, group I being the lightest work and group V the heaviest labor. From this study he concluded that the death rates for both indoor and outdoor workers were roughly independent of the degree of labor up to age forty-five, but that after that age there was an increased mortality among the heaviest labor groups; this increased mortality became very pronounced at the older age groups.

This work has been widely quoted as proving the deleterious effect of hard work, at least among older persons. However, after a study of the data, this reviewer remains very skeptical. A representative set of data from this work is reproduced in Table I. Pearl himself indicated that the data for age groups beyond sixty-five years of age was unreliable and he included it only for completeness. Then only the fifty-five to sixty-four age group shows any real increase at the highest labor grade, and even so the value is no higher than for group II. Further, on examining the labor performed by the men in group IV, it was found there were such trades as agricultural workers, stone

TABLE I

MEAN DEATH RATES PER 1000 AT THE AGES INDICATED FOR OUTDOOR WORKERS IN THE LABOR CATEGORIES INDICATED (FROM PEARL, 1924)

Labor group	Age group						65-74	75 and Over
	15-19	20-24	25-34	35-44	45-54	55-64		
I	1.27	2.45	3.57	6.02	11.29	23.49	52.58	163.00
II	1.63	3.16	4.05	7.38	13.97	29.30	67.62	174.93
III	1.29	2.97	4.51	6.34	11.64	23.88	56.39	162.20
IV	1.46	2.60	3.61	6.17	10.77	22.70	52.91	177.25
V	1.83	2.64	3.44	6.21	12.71	29.31	77.37	211.07

quarriers, railway engine stokers, etc. which seemed very little different from the men in group V. Yet the table shows group IV workers to be as long-lived as those of group I. Certainly if the concept were valid, one should see a progressive increase in death rate in the more strenuous labor categories with age from early adulthood onward. This is certainly not evident in Pearl's data, and no other data has been obtained on this important point.

Pearl further analyzed the data to take into account the differences in social class, and felt that this did not enter as a factor in evaluating the data. Again, one must view this with some skepticism.

The results do suggest that if men are forced to undertake extremely heavy labor beyond age sixty-five, the mortality rate is somewhat higher. Even if this is true, it does not seem surprising since very heavy labor at any age (see below) is conducive to a high mortality rate, and moderately heavy labor among men over sixty-five could be considered in the same category. If hard labor is truly a contributing factor in senescence it should become increasingly apparent in data such as those presented in Table I from early adulthood onward.

It is interesting to note that the one very positive result which emerged from this study was that the death rate for all outdoor workers was slightly lower than for all indoor workers of all ages up to age sixty-five, at which point the data became unreliable. This is the era in which tuberculosis took a heavy toll, and these results can be explained in part, at least, on this basis.

The conclusion reasonably drawn from this study would indicate that labor, *per se*, as it was performed in England during the first part of this century, did not contribute to senescence. It is thus difficult to cite this as evidence favoring the rate of living theory.

On the other hand, it does seem to be a fact that extremely hard work apparently leads to an early death. Pearl cites evidence indicating that Chinese treadmill-coolies live very short lives, and such trades as Chinese lumber sawyers, marble polishers, etc., do not lend themselves to long life. The term of a chair-bearer was eight years, and of a rickshaw runner, four years. However, these are special cases and in modern western society they have no parallel.

In summary, it seems that Pearl has failed to produce convincing evidence that, in the human, each individual has a total energy quota which he is free to use rapidly or slowly. Surely in the studies cited on various labor groups in England there must have been a difference well over a factor of two in total metabolism of these groups, yet the difference in longevity was questionable. However, studies on human populations preclude rigid controls and other factors may play dominant roles. For example, the harder working classes are, in general, the poorer ones, and their food intake relative to their metabolism may have been lower than their more affluent controls. The increased life span caused by the caloric-restricted diet may have just offset a life-shortening effect of the exercise. Thus it would be well to reserve judgment on this important concept.

INCREASED METABOLISM

As mentioned earlier, Rubner (1908) studied the metabolism of a wide variety of animals and concluded that the life span is roughly proportional to the total metabolism of the animal computed on a per gram basis. Thus the life span of man is roughly thirty times the life span of the mouse, yet they both expend about 700 calories per gram of tissue over their lifetimes. This comes about because the surface to volume ratio of man is much lower than that of the mouse and, therefore, the metabolism per gram can be much lower and still maintain the same body temperature, since heat loss is largely a surface phenomenon. The shrew is even smaller than the mouse, has a fantastic appetite, and probably has a maximum life span of one year. Such other data as exists for life spans and metabolisms of other animals seems to confirm this general idea. It is as if each gram of tissue had a certain amount of fuel which could be burned before running out. This general relation may be merely coincidental, but it is of such general occurrence it is hard to ignore.

Two recent experiments, one by Carlson *et al.* (1957) and one by Johnson *et al.* (1961) are very important in this regard. They kept rats throughout most of their life spans at quite cold temperatures, so the animals had to increase their metabolisms by about 30 per cent in order to maintain their body temperatures. It was found that the life spans of these animals was decreased considerably. The interesting thing is that they did not die of respiratory infection, as might be expected, but all causes of death were accelerated. Even cancer induction was hastened by causing the increased metabolism. This would seem to correlate beautifully with the ideas of Rubner and also with the fact that animals, like the fruit fly, have a life span dependent on their metabolism as regulated by the environmental temperature.

On the other hand, as just discussed, when the metabolism of the human is changed by hard work by more than a factor of two, the effect on the longevity is equivocal. Possibly muscle is not involved in the aging process, so an increase in metabolism in this organ alone, as in exercise, does not shorten the life span. This explanation seems quite inadequate, but the true one will have to await further clarification. In the meantime, the concept of the total metabolism as a cause of aging must surely be taken into account in any complete theory of senescence.

SELYE'S STRESS THEORY

For a number of years Selye (1956) has placed primary emphasis on stress as a causitive agent in aging. He has subjected rats to a wide variety of stress agents such as keeping them in the cold, prolonged trauma in a tumbling cage, long exposure to very loud noises, etc. These were very severe stresses for the animal and usually led to exhaustion. Many internal organs showed remarkable changes. The adrenal glands were often three times the normal size, and gastric ulcers were common. He also used large doses of hormones to cause serious derangements of the physiological mechanisms of animals. Many vascular accidents can occur under severe stress. Any or all of these conditions caused by stress can be severe enough to cause death, and in general the older animal will succumb to a given stress sooner than will a young one.

On the basis of these experiments Selye has developed the stress theory of aging which is really a variant of the wear and tear theory, and in fact, he looks upon the everyday stress of living as the rate of wear and tear on the body. He draws a sharp distinction between chronologic age and physiologic age. The physiologic age is determined by the total amount of wear and tear to which the body has been exposed. The wear and tear of life gradually uses up the vitality with which one is originally endowed, like spending one's inheritance. He feels that, to a large extent, the individual person can decide how fast he wants to use up his vitality, very much as did Pearl. If he uses it very slowly, he will be little more than a vegetable; if too fast, he will have an energetic but short life. When a person is exposed to a stressful situation, a good rest will almost, but not quite, return him to normal. Each event leaves a small residual deficit of adaptation energy, and day after day these deficits add up to cause aging. As modern medicine has pushed up the average life span, an increasing proportion of the population is dying from the degenerative diseases which are caused by wear and tear, i.e., stress.

In many respects this forms a very satisfying picture. However, it should be pointed out that it is largely conjecture from only a few relevant experiments. It is certainly true that excessive stress, even purely mental trauma, can cause death in both animals and man. It is also true that death caused in that way is often indistinguishable pathologically from death due to "natural causes." The same can be said, however, of a wide variety of different agents and conditions. If, for example, an animal or man lives under very unsanitary conditions, he will have his life expectancy shortened thereby, but one could hardly say that he is aging faster. As discussed in the first chapter, senescence must be considered not merely as something which leads to death, but as the deteriorative process which renders the individual increasingly susceptible to disease. Selye has not produced experimental evidence to indicate that there is an accumulation of deficits which cannot be erased by a period of rest. It is thus not possible to accept these ideas without further substantiation by experimental methods.

It should be noted that Selye's work is very important in showing the relation between stress and disease, or more specifically the part played by the nervous system in the etiology of many diseases.

DISEASE AND AGING

There is an old belief, probably dating back many centuries, that each time an individual suffers from a disease, even though he may apparently completely recover from the disease, it nevertheless leaves its mark on him and his life expectancy is shortened thereby. This belief is still widely held in many circles today, although the direct evidence bearing on this hypothesis is practically nonexistent. Extending this concept to the aging process, it would mean that senescence is caused by the sum of the various diseases and insults to which an individual is subject, and each one weakens him some and makes him more likely to contract and succumb to another. This concept is very similar to that put forward by Selye, and Jones (1956) has conducted an extensive actuarial study on different human populations in an effort to bring evidence to bear on this point. When he plots the age-specific death rates for the population of any country (Fig. 3) he finds that the death rate has been decreasing steadily for many years in the younger ages, and much less so in the older age groups. This is unquestionably due to progressively better sanitary conditions, better and more food, better medical care, etc. Jones reasons that the decreased mortality in the older age groups is at least partly due to the fact that they were not subject to as much disease when they were young. He concludes that ". . . the way to avoid disease is never to have disease."

Jones has reached this conclusion from two analyses of the mortality curves. First, is the fact that countries like Sweden have low disease rates and death rates in the young age groups, and also low death rates in the older age groups. On the other hand, a population like that of India has a very high disease rate in the young age groups and also a high mortality rate in the older groups. In other words, taking the age-specific death rates as a measure of the physiological age, it is found that this age is greater for a given chronological age in populations with a high disease rate. This is, of course, true, but the argument is open to the objection that the disease rate is also higher in the older age groups as well as the younger, and perhaps this is the reason for the higher age-specific mortality rate.

To get around this, Jones has made a cohort analysis of several populations over a long period of time. In such an analysis, ideally one would compare the mortality curves for a group of people living in a country all of whom were born in, say, 1850, with a similar group, all of whom were born in 1900. The older group would have had a much more severe disease experience, and Jones' curves seem to show a somewhat higher age-specific death rate at the older chronological ages in this group. This would seem to substantiate Jones' contention that disease leads to more disease. However, the curves are quite unconvincing. In the first place, the disease experience did not change markedly until the early part of this century, and there has not been enough time for the people born in 1910 to become very old. The curves are very incomplete. Further, by this analysis the disease experience of the population born in the middle of the 19th century would have changed sharply as it approached old age, thus skewing the curve at the older ages, while the populations born at the turn of the century were having their mortality curves skewed at the younger ages. Further, it is apparent that there are some diseases like rheumatic heart disease and tuberculosis, for which, at least for many years, there was no real cure. It is then to be expected that if such diseases are included in an analysis, the populations with a high disease incidence in the young will also have a somewhat higher incidence in the old age groups.

For these reasons, perhaps the best that can be done is to compare a reasonably stable population at two different times which reflect differences in disease experience. This is done for

Swedish males in Figure 3. It is seen that the curves converge at the older age groups, indicating again that the disease experience of youth has little effect on the longevity.

These curves also show that, whereas modern medicine has increased the average life span remarkably, it has done so by decreasing the mortality in the younger groups. The life expectancy for persons in the older age groups apparently has not changed appreciably. There is another piece of evidence tending to indicate that there is a ceiling on the life span of man which is unaffected, so far, by medical science. Korenchevsky (1961) has collected data on the number of persons living 100 years or more during the period 1900 to 1953 in England and Wales. During this period there was no increase in the numbers of males in this group, and only a questionable increase in females. During this same period the life expectancy of young adults increased dramatically.

This, then, argues against the concept that the longevity of a population is determined by the disease experience of its youth. It would indicate instead that the degenerative process goes on independently of the death rate at younger ages. If the environment is a very healthy one, many more people live to become senescent.

For these reasons it appears to this reviewer that there is no concrete evidence indicating that a disease, from which there is apparent complete recovery, leaves a residual damage which contributes to aging. In other words, disease, as such, apparently does not cause aging.

There is another very interesting side to the death rate curves. Jones (1960) has plotted the curves for various causes of death as a function of age, and has found that deaths from virtually all diseases follow a straight line function on a Gompertz plot. They do not all have the same slope or absolute values, but the slopes are not vastly different for the different diseases such as cancer, hypertension, nephrosis, etc. This would seem to indicate again that the body's resistance to all disease is decreasing with age, and which one actually causes demise is largely a matter of chance. This is another example of the deteriorative process we call senescence.

CHEMICAL STRESS

Most of the ideas discussed in this chapter so far postulate that stress, in one form or another, is responsible for the deterioration which takes place with time. In our laboratory we undertook to obtain experimental verification of this idea by means of chemical stresses. This type of stress can be accurately quantitated, repeated as often as desired, and when it is no longer administered, the animal is free of the stress and can deal with the consequences of the stress in an uncomplicated manner. It is known that ionizing radiation causes a shortening of the life span and apparently an acceleration of the process of senescence. According to the stress theory, the radiation is merely acting as a stress. In many of these chemical stress experiments the stressed animals were compared for longevity with irradiated animals in an attempt to discern similarities or dissimilarities between chemical and radiation stresses.

The chemical stresses consisted mostly of bacterial toxins or toxoids which could be injected into the mice to cause all the signs and symptoms of the particular disease. Since the bacteria were not present, however, complete recovery was achieved as soon as the injections were stopped. The stresses chosen were, so far as possible, generalized stresses, in that the toxin or chemical affected all the organs of the body and did not weaken any one of them more than the others.

These stresses can be accurately quantitated; the dose necessary to kill half of the animals (LD_{50}) can be determined, and the experimental group of animals given gradations of this dose. The animals are then allowed to live out their lives under carefully regulated laboratory conditions, and their longevity compared to that of their controls.

Figure 4 shows the result of one such experiment, demonstrating that a single severe chemical stress is not effective in shortening the life span, whereas radiation does so very markedly. All chemical stresses tried so far give the same result, and likewise with only a very minor exception, all forms of ionizing radiation cause an apparent acceleration of aging (Curtis and Healey, 1957).

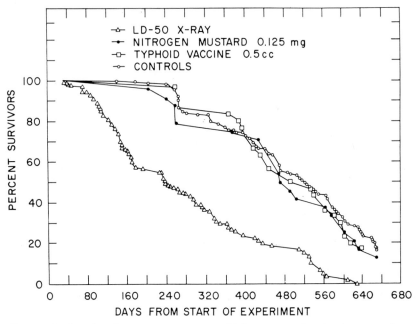

Figure 4. Results of an experiment in which groups of animals were given half-lethal doses of x rays, nitrogen mustard, or typhoid toxoid when eight weeks of age. After thirty days the survivors were kept until natural death. The chemical stresses produce no premature senescence in sharp contrast to that produced by x rays (from data of Curtis and Healey, 1957).

Small doses of radiation repeated at frequent intervals, or administered continuously at a low level, will add up to produce a marked shortening of the life span. It is entirely possible that a single chemical stress would not be enough to cause an appreciable shortening of the life span, but if repeated often enough could add up to do so. Consequently, a series of experiments were undertaken in which the chemical stress was repeated as often as possible without killing the animal. The results of one such experiment are shown in Figure 5. Here an almost lethal dose of nitrogen mustard was administered twice a week for the lifetime of the animal, and there was only a slightly higher mortality rate than for the controls—it is doubtful if there is a significant difference. However, when a third of this dose was given twice a week it constituted a severe and prolonged

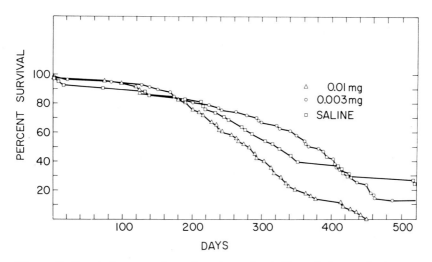

Figure 5. Survival curves for mice given the indicated doses of nitrogen mustard twice a week from age eight weeks. Each dose is almost fatal, but they produce no statistically significant decrease in life span (from Stevenson and Curtis, 1961).

stress and there was definitely no effect on the survival (Stevenson and Curtis, 1961).

Another such experiment is shown in Figure 6. Here doses of tetanus toxoid and tetanus toxin were given every fourteen days to groups of mice. Since the mice developed an immunity to this toxin, another group of mice was treated in the same way as the experimental group in each case, and each time before the experimental group was injected, a small sample from the other group was used to determine the LD_{50} dose of the toxin at that time. The experimental group was then given half of this dose. In this way there was assurance that the mice received a severe stress each time. The stress was continued for almost a year and there was only a suggestion that the tetanus toxin treatment caused some mortality in that series. There was no effect with these doses of toxoid. The important thing to observe from the experiment is that when the stress was removed, there was no increased mortality in the treated groups. In other words, this severe and prolonged stress, once it had been

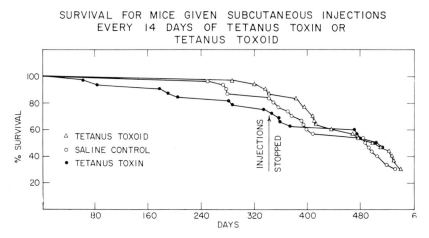

Figure 6. Survival curves for mice receiving large but nonfatal doses every fourteen days of the agents indicated for a large fraction of their life spans. These severe stresses did not alter the life expectancy of the animals after the treatments were stopped (from Curtis and Gebhard, 1958).

removed, left the animals with as long a life expectancy as if they had never been stressed (Curtis and Gebhard, 1958a).

Very much the same results were obtained with other stress agents. Mice were given subcutaneous injection of sterile turpentine to form large sterile ulcers which gradually broke down to form large open sores. As soon as a mouse had recovered sufficiently another sterile ulcer was formed in another area. As would be expected, some of the mice died of infection. After about a year, the treatments were stopped and it was found, as before, the life expectancy of these mice was the same as that of the controls (Curtis and Gebhard, 1958a).

These experiments indicated quite clearly that a generalized stress *per se*, even though it was repeated often over a long period of time, did not cause the deterioration characteristic of senescence. From this, it must be concluded that the accumulation of stresses is not the cause of senescence in the normal animal.

It should be noted that Alexander and Connell (1960) and also Conklin *et al.* (1963) found that when they gave repeated doses of some of the so-called radiomimetic drugs to mice, they caused a shortening of the life span. These drugs included ethyl methane sulfonate, myleran and nitrogen mustard. However, when Curtis and Healey (1957) and Stevenson and Curtis (1961) used nitrogen mustard, they found no measurable shortening of the life span. Since the positive results reported by the other groups were not very large, one can attribute the differences to the different strains of mice used. In any event, it seems that these agents almost certainly shorten the life span by the same mechanism as does radiation since they are, like radiation, very potent mutagenic agents. These experiments will be discussed further with the treatment of the mutation theory of aging. They should thus be considered as specific stresses, and not as the generalized stresses being discussed here.

It would be a mistake to carry this conclusion to extremes. There certainly is a deteriorative process which we call senescence which is characterized by a weakened condition of one or more organs. Each individual has his own weak link. There are strains of mice which die, predominantly, of nephosclerosis. Undoubtedly if the kidneys of these mice were injured in such a way that they could not fully recover, their life span would be shortened because their weak link would have been weakened and the deteriorative process would not have had to go so far in breaking it. One can imagine, for example, that mercury poisoning would have destroyed half the nephrons in these mice, and they are not regenerated. As the nephrosclerotic process advanced, destroying more and more nephrons, there would soon come a time when there were too few nephrons to support life. One can imagine many other similar situations.

However, such speculations should not be allowed to dilute the conclusion that stress is not the causative agent in senescence. In the above example, the process responsible for the nephrosclerosis should be considered the primary causitive agent, and the mercury poisoning stress as a secondary factor. The people of India have a much shorter life expectancy than people in the western world because the incidence of contagious diseases is so much higher. However, there is no evidence that the basic process of senescence proceeds any faster in these people than in any others.

SUMMARY

When one breaks down the wear and tear theory into the two components, the rate of living part consisting specifically of the total cellular metabolism, and the pure stress part, the picture becomes more clear. It appears that the stress component can be ruled out as a causitive factor.

However, the picture is not nearly so clear as far as metabolism is concerned. All experiments which have been performed on this to date, as far as mammals are concerned, are rather inconclusive. This is especially true of the studies on humans. Such evidence as exists seems to argue in favor of the idea that, at least to some extent, an organism is endowed with a certain metabolic capacity, and when this capacity is used up it can no longer support life. It will be well to reserve judgment on this important point awaiting further evidence.

Chapter 4

THE MUTATION THEORY

A S INDICATED earlier, this theory has been advanced rather recently, and it has only been within the past five years that there has been definite experimental evidence bearing on it. The basic concept of the theory is simple. It postulates that spontaneous mutations are produced in the somatic cells of the mammal and, since all mutations cause the cell to function somewhat differently, the various organs would gradually become filled with cells which were able to perform different functions than those of the original organ. The cells of the young organ were evolved to perform the function of that organ efficiently; any change would probably be for the worse.

The idea behind this theory has only recently been formulated in definite terms by Failla (1958), Curtis and Gebhard (1958b) and Szilard (1959). Failla assumes that when a cell suffers a mutation it becomes ineffective and the animal loses vitality. As many others have done, he computed the numbers of mutations to be expected in somatic cells based on the known mutation rates for the germ cells, and found this gives far too few mutations to account for senescence. He then assumed that the mutation rate for somatic cells is given by the relation $e^{\alpha t}$ where α is the slope of the mortality curve on the Gompertz plot. From this he then deduces that the spontaneous mutation rate for somatic cells must be twelve times that for germ cells. He has no experimental evidence to prove or disprove the hypothesis, but he presents very convincing logical arguments why it is probably true.

Szilard, on the other hand, presents a highly original mathematical model of aging based on the mutation concept. He, too, found that if one takes mutation rates from germ cells and applies

41

them to somatic cells, there are not enough mutated cells to begin to account for senescence. He then postulates that "hits" can occur in the genes of a chromosome which render them inactive, and this constitutes a "fault." When a fault occurs in a diploid cell in both of a pair of genes, the character controlled by that gene becomes deficient and if the character is essential, the cell either becomes inefficient or dies. Each individual is assumed to start life with a certain number of faults, and these increase as the number of hits accumulate. In order to get some idea as to the number of initial faults and their rate of increase, he compared the difference in time of death for identical twins to that for members of the rest of the population. From these and many other assumptions for which there was very little concrete evidence, he worked out a relation which can be used to predict, for example, the amount by which radiation in various forms could be expected to decrease life expectancy. The trouble with this theory is that there are many unknown constants which must be evaluated before the theory can be tested, and these are very difficult to establish. It has stimulated a good deal of thought on the subject, and many of the suggestions will no doubt be found useful in the future.

However, as pointed out by Maynard-Smith (1959), there are a number of objections to Szilard's theory. The life span of inbred strains of animals tend to be shorter than the hybrids. Since inbreds are homozygous, the theory would predict that it would take more, not less, time to inactivate both sets of homologous chromosomes. Also, *Drosophila* raised at 30° C have a much shorter life span than those raised at 20° C. If they are raised at 30° C for the first half of their life, and at 20° C for the last half, the life span is the same as if they had been raised at 20° C for the entire time. Again this is contrary to the theory, since they should have acquired faults at 30° C which would have shortened their life.

These objections are difficult to answer but need not invalidate the theory. The phenomenon of hybrid vigor is one which has puzzled geneticists for half a century, so it would be unwise to draw hasty conclusions on the basis of this objection. Further, as Szilard points out, aging in insects may be quite different from aging in mammals, so one should not take Maynard-Smith's objections too seriously on that basis either.

RADIATION INDUCED AGING

For a number of years one of the strongest arguments in favor of the somatic mutation theory of aging was the discovery, made during the war in connection with the development of atomic energy (Henshaw *et al.*, 1946), that animals subjected to ionizing radiations appear to age more rapidly, and do indeed have a shorter life expectancy than their controls. At autopsy it was found that, in general, the same diseases which are responsible for the death of normal animals are also responsible for the death of irradiated animals, but they contract the diseases sooner. In other words, it appears that radiation has accelerated the development of the degenerative diseases (Figs. 7 and 8). This finding has since been confirmed many times in a number of laboratories.

At first it was felt that the radiation was merely acting as a carcinogenic agent and speeding cancer induction. However, if one subtracts all deaths due to cancer, one still finds an increase in the mortality rate over that of the controls (Alexander, 1957). Also, Upton (1957) showed that the development of nephrosclerosis in mice was accelerated by radiation. Recently Lindop and Rotblat (1961) have re-examined the question using large numbers of mice and careful autopsies and concluded that with few exceptions the general concept is correct. All forms of degenerative disease are accelerated, but some are accelerated more than others.

There are objections to considering this phenomenon as a true acceleration of aging. Since no one can accurately define aging, it is impossible to say it has been accelerated. Also, there are some phenomena usually associated with aging that do not appear to be affected by radiation, and vice versa. There is a strain of rat which is very susceptible to the development of benign hepatomas, and these are apparently not accelerated by radiation (Connell and Alexander, 1959). There are also strains

Figure 7. Photographs of two groups of fourteen-month-old mice which originally had been identical. The control mice on the left are normal and healthy. The group on the right received a large but nonfatal dose of radiation when they were young adults; only three are left in this group and they are old and senile (from Curtis, 1963a).

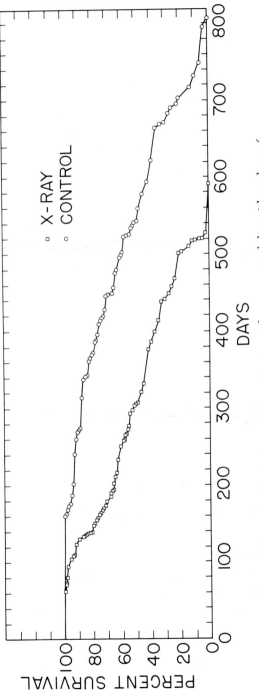

Figure 8. Survival curve for mice treated as young adults with a dose of 650 r of x rays, and for their controls (from Stevenson and Curtis, 1961).

of black mice that do not develop gray hair as they age, but radiation readily turns the hair gray. Again, Kohn and Guttman (1963) found the tumor spectrum was somewhat different in irradiated mice as compared to controls and on these grounds objected to the concept. It seems to this reviewer that, since aging is undoubtedly a very complex biological process, it would be much too much to expect to find any agent that would accelerate all the signs and symptoms of aging equally. By emphasizing the many similarities between natural and radiation induced aging, one can hope to learn more about both.

When different types of radiation are administered to animals in different dosage regimes, the shortening of the life span varies for each different treatment. A great deal is known about the effect of these radiations on living systems. Much progress has been made by using radiation as a method for changing the rate of aging, and it has served as a very effective test for theories of aging.

CHROMOSOME ABERRATIONS

The experimental approach to the mutation theory has been difficult because there is no way of measuring mutations in somatic cells of animals. In plants the situation is simpler because the somatic cells will eventually differentiate to form the germ cells. Therefore, if a mutation exists or is induced in the somatic cells, it can be detected in subsequent generations in the usual way. Thus Caldecott (1961) exposed seeds of young plants to radiations and measured the increased mutation rate in the next generation. He also examined the dividing cells of the meristem microscopically and scored the various aberrations observed. Figure 9 shows a curve drawn from his data showing an approximate linear relationship between chromosome aberrations and mutations produced in the next generation. This does not mean that each aberration is represented by a mutation, but on the average, one can say that the chromosome aberrations are proportional to the mutations produced, or the aberrations can be taken as an index of the number of mutations present.

There is every reason to believe that this same relation holds true for animals as well as plants. Thus if chromosome aberra-

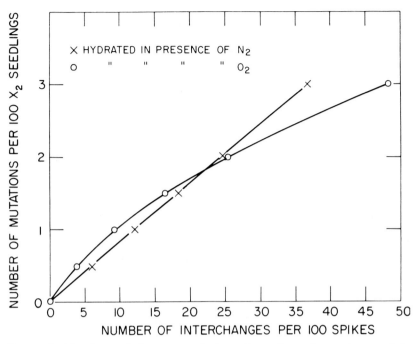

Figure 9. Numbers of chromosomal aberrations (interchanges) scored in root tip cells of seedlings grown from x-irradiated barley seeds, plotted against the mutation frequency scored in the succeeding generation. This shows there is a reasonable correlation between the chromosomal aberrations produced by a given treatment and the true mutations present in the cells (from data by Caldecott, 1961).

tions are scored in somatic cells of animals, this value could be used as an index of the mutations present.

This has been done in a rather extensive series of experiments using liver cells in mice as the ones studied (Curtis, 1963). These cells very seldom divide in the normal animal, but by partially destroying the liver, the remaining cells will immediately start to undergo division. One can sacrifice the animal at the height of regeneration, at which time many of the liver cells will be in the act of cell division. A small piece of the liver is then minced, a cell "squash" preparation made on a microscopic slide, and the chromosomal material stained (Stevenson and Curtis, 1961). The entire cell nucleus appears on the slide, and only those cells appearing in anaphase are scored. Almost all the cells observed in division are liver parenchymal cells, and those few reticuloendothelial cells and others occasionally seen in division in the preparations are easy to identify as being different from parenchymal cells and they are ignored. There is a very small error due to scoring incorrect cell types.

In viewing the anaphase figures, the two daughter nuclei are just pulling apart and one can often see bridges between them composed of chromosomes which did not separate cleanly at metaphase. They will eventually be pulled apart as cell division continues. This is indicative of something very wrong with one or more chromosomes. In addition, one can often see pieces of chromosome (fragments) which have broken off and are not taking part in the division. The slides are always scored for bridges and fragments separately. However, it has been almost

Figure 10. Photomicrograph of an abnormal dividing liver cell in anaphase. The two daughter nuclei are still joined by three chromosome strands which will eventually break, and there are three pieces of chromosomes which do not take part in the mitosis. In the mitosis of a normal nucleus all chromosomes take part in the division and pull apart cleanly (from Curtis, 1963a).

universally found that the two go together so closely that for the final reporting of the data any cell having one or more bridges or fragments is scored as abnormal. One abnormal anaphase figure is illustrated in Figure 10. This method has been adapted from work by Albert (1958) and others.

It should be pointed out that the method has a number of shortcomings. The scoring of aberrations is done at the limit of resolution of the light microscope. Under these conditions different observers tend to score differently. The same observer will vary his scoring from one day to the next and even at various times during the same day. Also, each different strain of mouse will exhibit a characteristic chromosome aberration frequency. For these reasons it is necessary to perform the experiments with very rigid controls, and to score the slides "blind." A single experiment can validly answer a single question, but it is not valid to make quantitative comparisons from one experiment to another.

Another difficulty in the quantitative interpretation of these experiments lies in the fact that it is only possible to score a cell as either normal or abnormal provided one can view it in the act of cell division. However, cells with abnormal chromosomes cannot be induced to divide as readily as can normal cells. In any situation in which the chromosomes have been damaged, either naturally or artificially, proportionately fewer numbers of abnormal cells will be scored than normals. Consequently, the percentage of abnormalities scored will always be too low for that reason. Following even a moderate dose of radiation, and especially following a large dose, it is found that the percentage abnormalities increases for as long as 100 days. This can be explained by the well known fact that radiation causes either a delay or an inhibition of cell division in the damaged cells. At first the damaged cells are not scored and the aberration percentage observed is too low. As the cells recover, it becomes possible to force a larger percentage of abnormal cells into division, and the measured values increase. For these reasons it is difficult to make quantitative comparisons in the aberration frequency even though there were rigid controls. For example, if it were observed that a certain treatment doubled the observed aberration frequency, it could not be concluded that the real aberration frequency had been doubled; it would have been more than doubled, but how much more is rather uncertain.

Another source of quantitative uncertainty lies in the fact that any cell having a bridge or a fragment, or several of each, is scored as abnormal. In a heavily damaged cell population, many of the cells scored as abnormal will have multiple chromosomal injuries. Here again, in comparing a damaged cell population with its control, the increase in observed per cent abnormality will not completely reflect the increased damage.

This method has been used to obtain a good deal of evidence bearing on the mutation theory. First, it was found that there is a steady increase in chromosome aberrations with age (Stevenson and Curtis, 1961). This is shown in Figure 11, and is a consistent

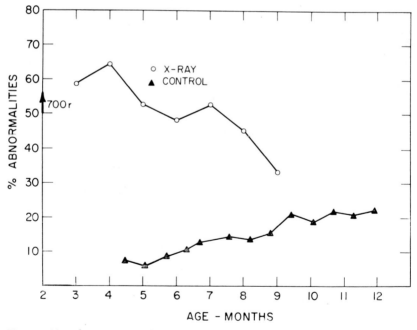

Figure 11. Chromosome aberrations in liver cells as a function of age in normal mice and in mice which had received a large dose of x rays (from Stevenson and Curtis, 1961).

finding in all groups of mice. When the mice in this experiment were only twelve months old, the aberrations reached 22 per cent. If 22 per cent of the chromosomes were so grossly abnormal that the abnormality could be detected with a light microscope, there surely were many more cells with abnormal chromosomes, and it does not seem unreasonable to postulate that virtually every cell in these animals carried at least one mutation at that time. As the mice grow older, the percentages keep increasing until, in some strains, 75 per cent of all cells have grossly abnormal cell divisions.

Next it was found that following a single dose of x ray large enough to shorten the life expectancy of the animals appreciably, there was a sudden increase in aberrations which decreased very slowly over a period of many months. This is also shown in Figure 11 and, of course, greatly strengthens the concept that the animals receiving the radiation will age more rapidly because the chromosomes of the cells were damaged.

It has been known for many years that the administration of x or gamma ray radiation at a very low dose rate is only about one quarter as effective in shortening the life span as is the same dose administered in a single acute dose. In a series of experiments, Curtis and Crowley (1963) found that chromosome aberrations develop quite slowly when gamma rays are administered at a low rate, and indeed, for equal doses, are only one quarter as effective in producing chromosome aberrations as are single doses (Fig. 12).

On the other hand, it is well known that neutrons produce quite different effects. Low dose rates are equally as effective in shortening the life span as are high dose rates. In a recent experiment (Curtis *et al.*, 1964), it was found that the same is true for the development of chromosome aberrations (Fig. 13).

It has also been noted from these and other curves that for equal doses, neutrons are about twice as effective in producing chromosome aberrations as are x rays. This is also the ratio of effectiveness of these two radiations in producing shortening of the life span.

Thus, for all types of radiations and radiation regimes, the

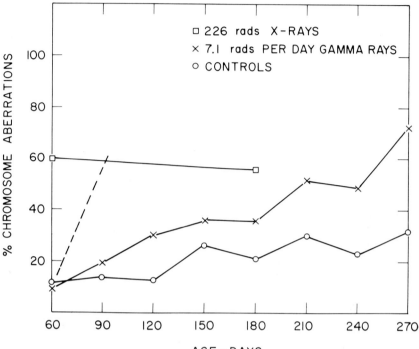

Figure 12. Chromosome aberrations in liver cells of mice subjected to chronic gamma and acute x-irradiation, and their controls. The dashed line gives the expected rate of accumulation of aberrations for chronically irradiated mice assuming that chronic is just as effective in producing aberrations as is acute irradiation. Since the experimental line is far from the theoretical one, the assumption is not valid (from Curtis and Crowley, 1963).

degree of life shortening produced is quantitatively related to the amount of chromosomal damage produced by each. It would be a rare coincidence if there were not a causal relation between them.

CHROMOSOMAL ABNORMALITIES INDICATIVE OF CONGENITAL DISEASES

In recent years there has been a good deal of evidence to indicate that specific diseases are caused by specific defects in the chromosome structure of the individual. These are de-

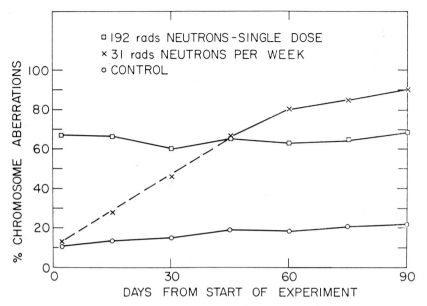

Figure 13. Chromosome aberrations in liver cells of mice subjected to chronic and acute neutron irradiation, and their controls. The dashed line shows the rate of build-up of chromosome aberrations if chronic were as effective as is acute neutron irradiation. Since the experimental points fall close to the dashed line it is concluded this is true (from Curtis, Tilley and Crowley, 1964a).

termined by culturing the white blood cells of an individual and when the cells are in active division, plating out the cells by the squash technique to observe the chromosomes in metaphase. Each individual chromosome can be identified and any abnormality in either shape or number noted. It has been found, for example, that trisomy in chromosome twenty-one in the human is always found in cases of mongolism. This technique is now being used rather extensively as a diagnostic aid as well as an indication of the etiology of many diseases.

The concept is based on the idea that a mutation has taken place in one of the germ cells of the parents, or in very early embryonic life, so all cells of the individual carry the same defect. The chromosome aberrations discussed in this monograph are produced in the individual cells after birth and presumably are different in every cell. Particular techniques used for examining the cells, metaphase *vs* anaphase figures, insures that the two different origins of the aberrations will be distinguished from each other.

The specific chromosome aberrations scored at metaphase constitute a separate study in themselves and merit an extensive treatise. However, they have very little bearing on the problem at hand and will not be considered further in this monograph.

CHEMICAL MUTAGENS

It is quite obvious that if the mutation theory is correct, the chemical mutagens should cause shortening of the life span as well as radiation. Consequently, a series of experiments was undertaken with the chemical mutagen nitrogen mustard. This compound was known to break chromosomes in bone marrow cells, intestinal epithelium, and testes; this is the basis on which it has been used as a chemotherapeutic agent for leukemia and other neoplasms. In the first experiment (Fig. 4) a single dose designed to kill about half the animals was administered and the survivors followed for their natural lives. No effect was observed.

It was then felt that the cytotoxic effect of the drug would perhaps be so great that it would mask the genetic effects in the somatic cells. Consequently, almost lethal doses of the drug were given to a group of mice twice weekly over almost the entire life span of the mice (Fig. 5). Again there was no effect on the life span. This would seem to be a very serious blow to the mutation theory, since it seems to run quite contrary to the theory and to the radiation results.

Consequently, a third experiment was undertaken in which an almost lethal dose of nitrogen mustard was again administered twice a week for the entire life of the animals (Stevenson and Curtis, 1961). Again there was no significant change in life expectancy. In addition, the liver cells of these mice were scored for chromosome aberrations (Fig. 14) and even after this very drastic treatment the chromosome aberrations increased only slightly faster than the controls, and indeed, a statistical analysis shows that the difference in slope of the three curves is just on

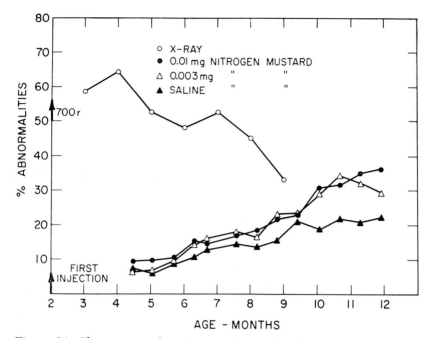

Figure 14. Chromosome aberrations in liver cells of mice given nitrogen mustard at two different levels twice a week for the duration of the experiment, and of saline injected controls. Data from mice given a single dose of x rays is shown for comparison. This drastic nitrogen mustard treatment increases the aberrations only slightly if at all (from Stevenson and Curtis, 1961).

the limit of statistical significance. It is quite unnecessary to apply a statistical analysis to the x-ray curve which is for only a single dose.

It appears then that nitrogen mustard does not affect the cells of the liver, whereas it certainly does affect those of the bone marrow and other organs. The difference appears to be that the organs in active cell division are affected, but at least insofar as the liver cells are representative of normally nondividing cells, one can say that nitrogen mustard does not affect them.

This, then, very largely removes the objection to the mutation theory posed by the original experiments. However, there have been other objections raised with respect to the chemical mutagens. It was found by Alexander and Connell (1960) and by Conklin *et al.* (1963) that myleran and some of the other chemical mutagens, when administered once a week for four weeks, did cause some shortening of the life span. Unfortunately, no data are available on the aberrations produced by these agents, so it is impossible to say now whether there is a correlation between aberrations and shortening of the life span for these agents. Alexander (1963) has found that with one of the newer chemical mutagens, ethylmethanesulfonate (EMS), which is said to be the most potent chemical mutagen known, there was no shortening of the life span. He reasoned that since there was no correlation between the mutagenicity of the compound and its ability to shorten the life span of mice, the shortening of the life span must be due to characteristics of the drugs other than their mutagenicity. He defines mutation rather narrowly as being a point mutation, and is ready to concede that agents which break chromosomes probably shorten the life span by this mechanism. It should be pointed out that the mutagenicity of these compounds is tested on the mold, *Neurospora*, or on *Drosophila*. It is known that the behavior of these compounds is highly dependent on many ancillary conditions such as pH, oxygen tension, etc., so it seems highly likely that they would behave quite differently when injected into a mouse than when applied to neurospora. It will be necessary to withhold judgment on this important point until more information is available.

At the present time, the only mutagenic compound (nitrogen mustard) known to cause chromosome breaks in bone marrow and similar cells, does not cause an appreciable shortening of the life span of mice and does not cause chromosome aberrations in liver cells. This is an important point and will be discussed later.

In summary, the available evidence indicates that in mammals, mutagenic agents may affect different cells differently. Apparently some agents affect one type and some another, although the evidence on this point is very uncertain. Certainly some agents shorten the life span of some strains of mice, but do not shorten the life of others. In the face of this much uncertainty, it would be very dangerous to use this evidence to either prove or disprove the mutation hypothesis of aging.

ABERRATIONS IN DIFFERENT STRAINS OF MICE

It is well known that two different inbred strains of mice may have different life expectancies, even though both may exhibit quite a wide spectrum of causes of death. In a recent experiment with two such strains it was shown (Crowley and Curtis, 1963) that the long lived strain (C57BL/6J) developed aberrations at a much slower rate than the short lived strain (A/HEJ) (Fig. 15). In these two strains the dramatic difference in life expectancy is correlated with the equally dramatic difference in the rate at which each develops chromosome aberrations with age.

Whereas this is the only experiment directly designed to test this point, it is interesting to note that the strain of mouse usually used in our laboratory, CD1, has a life expectancy midway between that of the two strains used for this experiment and develops aberrations at a rate about midway between them.

This experiment gives very strong support to the somatic

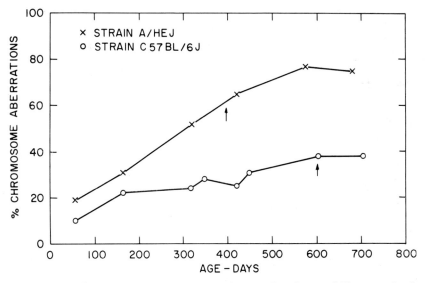

Figure 15. Chromosome aberrations in liver cells of two different inbred strains of mice, plotted as a function of age. The median life span of each strain is indicated by the arrows (data from Crowley and Curtis, 1963).

mutation theory of aging, but perhaps it should be accepted with some caution. It still represents data on only two strains of mice. While it appears that mutations are very important in the aging process, it would be surprising if there were not other factors which play important parts. If one of these other factors were determinant in limiting the life span for a particular strain, it would appear to invalidate the above conclusion. For example, the C58 strain of mouse develops leukemia at a very young age because of an inherited genetic character, and it would be surprising if this strain also developed chromosome aberrations in liver cells at a very high rate. We are thus again driven back to a definition of aging. This particular problem can be resolved only after the aberration rate as well as a complete mortality picture is obtained on a large number of different strains of mice. Until this analysis is accomplished it seems reasonable to consider the experiment presented in Figure 15 as strong evidence supporting the mutation theory.

There is other indirect evidence which has a distinct bearing on this question. Grahn (1958) has shown that, using quite a number of different inbred strains of mice, there is a very positive correlation between the dose of radiation necessary to produce lethality in a species and the longevity of that species (Fig. 16). He further showed that there is a direct relation between the dose necessary for acute lethality and the dose necessary to produce a given amount of shortening of the life span. In other words, an inbred strain of mice which is sensitive to radiation as indicated by acute lethality, is also sensitive as measured by life shortening or radiation induced aging. It has been pointed out several times previously that there is good evidence indicating that most radiation damage of interest biologically is that to the chromosomes. Further, it has been shown by Steffensen (1955) that when the spontaneous mutation rate in *Tradescantia* is changed by manipulation of the mineral nutrients, the radiation sensitivity to chromosomal damage is changed in a parallel fashion. Putting these facts together, it would seem justified to conclude that whatever factors are responsible for the stability of the chromosomes of various

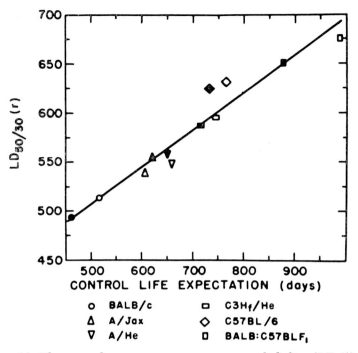

Figure 16. The x-ray dose necessary to cause acute lethality (LD 50/30) as a function of the normal life expectation for different strains of mice. Solid symbols represent males and open symbols, females (from Grahn, 1958).

strains of mice, some have somatic cells with rather stable chromosomes and some with rather unstable chromosomes. The stability of the chromosomes, as indicated here by the radiation sensitivity, is inversely related to the longevity. Whereas this is still not a proven relationship, it argues strongly for the mutation theory of aging.

These experiments are in accord with recent work of Jacobs *et al.* (1961) who examined the peripheral blood leucocytes of humans and found slightly fewer chromosomes per cell, on the average, for older persons than young ones. However, the difference in going from infants to very old people was slight and there was some question about the statistical significance of the finding. However, if true, it gives presumptive evidence that a chromosome aberration has occurred in the life of the cell line severe enough to eliminate an entire chromosome. Such cells would probably be eliminated by cell selection during cell division since this is an actively dividing tissue. It is not surprising that very few are observed even in very old people.

CHROMOSOMAL RECOVERY

It has been known in radiobiology for many years that, in general, a small dose of x rays is proportionately less effective in producing biological damage than a large dose. For example, if a certain dose is delivered to a dry seed and the seed then germinated and grown, the radiation damage can be accurately measured as the growth defect. Now, if half the dose is administered to similar seeds, and some hours later another half-dose is administered, the growth defect will be much less, indicating that a certain recovery took place from the first half-dose. This recovery process can be accurately studied for both the recovery time required and the relation to the size of the dose. The same phenomenon is observed when one administers radiation continuously at a low dose rate and compares the effect produced by a single acute dose of the same size. From such studies the "hit" theory of radiobiology has been formulated. According to this theory, ionizations (hits) occur in discrete parts of the cell, and it is these events which cause the damage. If one hit occurs in a part of a cell, and there are no other hits close to it in either space or time, then the cell has a good chance of repairing the damage. If, however, two or more hits occur too close together, in space and time, then the cell cannot deal with such extensive damage and it becomes irreparable. It seems eminently reasonable, and there is at least some evidence to support the idea, that the repair of the damage is an active metabolic process and cannot take place in the absence of oxygen (Wolf, 1961). The repair process also behaves as if it were controlled by enzymes (Howard-Flanders, 1964; Patrick and Haynes, 1964). These data are then subject to the interpretation that at large radiation doses the recovery mechanisms of the cell cannot keep up with the damage produced. Whatever the mechanism, there is no doubt that recovery from x-ray damage does take place over short periods of time following the irradiation.

No such phenomenon has been observed with neutron irradiation. Here the damage is almost entirely caused by recoil protons which produce dense ionization tracks in a cell. A cell structure which is hit by one of these is understandably damaged beyond repair.

It will be seen from Figure 12 that if γ rays are applied to a mouse at a low dose rate, chromosome aberrations are produced in the liver at only about a quarter the rate as if the radiation were administered acutely. Chromosome damage is subject to the same recovery processes as discussed above for damage to the whole cells.

On the other hand, Figure 17 shows that there is no recovery of chromosome damage in the liver following neutron irradiation, again substantiating the observations on cellular damage. These repair phenomena take place over relatively short periods of time (minutes or hours) and seem to be common to all types of cells including mammalian cells. This has recently been shown to be true also for true gene mutations in mice by Russell (1962, 1963) who demonstrated a marked dose rate effect on these

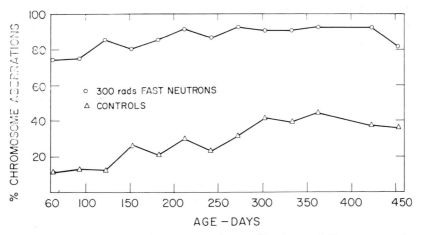

Figure 17. Chromosome aberrations in liver cells of mice following a single dose of neutrons, and their controls (from Curtis and Crowley, 1963).

mutations. From Figure 11 it will be seen that at least in liver cells there is a recovery which takes place over a period of many months. Since there is very little cell division in the liver it seems unlikely that the aberrant cells could be eliminated by cell selection during cell division, but some estimates of the mitotic rate seem to indicate that this was a possible explanation. However, the similar curves for neutron irradiation did not show any appreciable return to the control curve (Fig. 17) (Curtis and Crowley, 1963). If cell selection operated to eliminate aberrant cells from an x-irradiated liver, surely the same process would operate in the case of neutrons. Since it does not, it would seem that one must look for another explanation.

On the other hand, it would seem that as a general rule, cell selection must operate to eliminate aberrant cells. For example, when an animal receives a dose of radiation, one can see all manner of chromosome aberrations in the bone marrow cells. However, in a relatively few days practically all aberrations have disappeared, and since these cells are undergoing cell division quite rapidly, it seems almost certain that cell selection must operate to rid the marrow of aberrant cells.

Returning to the liver, an experiment was performed in an effort to clarify this situation (Curtis *et al.*, 1964). If a dose of carbon tetrachloride is administered to a mouse, part of the liver is destroyed, and it immediately starts to regenerate. A dose can be given which will destroy about 60 per cent of the liver, and in this experiment this dose was given to mice every forty-five days. There were four groups of mice; with and without a dose of radiation, and for each of these, a group with and without periodic administration of CCl_4. The results are shown in Figure 18. It will be seen that the animals in which the livers had been stimulated to regenerate often, eliminated their radiation induced aberrations more rapidly than if cell division had not been induced. However, it was not nearly as rapid as might be expected if aberrations are eliminated from the cell population after one cell division. One can compute the approximate shape of the recovery curve on the assumption that an aberrant cell is eliminated after one cell division, or after two cell divisions,

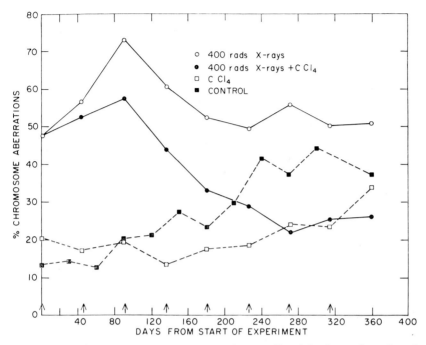

Figure 18. Chromosome aberrations in liver cells of both irradiated and control mice, and with and without carbon tetrachloride injections every forty-five days (arrows) which destroyed about half the liver. The induced cell division caused only a slow return to control levels (from Curtis, Tilley and Crowley, 1964b).

etc. A family of curves can be constructed on these different assumptions. When this is done, it appears that the experimental curve lies a little beyond the curve which was constructed, assuming the aberrant cells underwent four divisions before being eliminated. Of course this is very rough, but is accurate enough to indicate that a liver cell can undergo division several times even though the chromosomes are grossly abnormal, but that eventually cell selection will eliminate it.

This experiment means that in a normal situation following a dose of x-radiation, the return to control numbers of aberrations cannot be due to elimination by cell division and must be the result of some kind of spontaneous recovery process within the cell itself. The simplest explanation is that the recovery processes which seem to operate at short times following irradiation, continue to operate over very long periods. Apparently there is chromosomal damage which is so severe it takes a long time to heal, but will eventually do so. On the other hand, if the damage is still more severe, as that inflicted by neutrons, no recovery is possible within the life-time of the mouse.

This sort of a recovery phenomenon can also be demonstrated for true mutations in lower forms. Kimball *et al.* (1959) showed that when paramecia are put in a medium with very little food, the cell divisions are arrested. When first given a dose of radiation and food was then withheld, the number of mutations decreased steadily the longer the cells were kept from undergoing division. The same sort of effect was shown by Patrick *et al.* (1964) for yeast. This shows that in these lower forms the cells are able to repair a good deal of the damage inflicted by x rays, provided they are not required to undergo cell division.

These experiments leave us with a picture of the chromosome as a very labile structure which is apparently continually breaking down and repairing itself. Since aging is dependent on chromosome stability, the repair process is as important as the factors responsible for the injuries. Apparently the difference between a long-lived person and one who dies young lies in the stability of the chromosome structure, but it is not known whether it is an inherent stability or an efficient repair mechanism.

THE CAUSE OF SPONTANEOUS MUTATIONS

The cause of spontaneous mutations is still not known, but these and other experiments permit us to at least eliminate several possible causes. First, soon after the discovery of radiation mutageneses, it was supposed that the natural background radiation, made up of radiations from radioactive material in the earth plus the cosmic rays, caused the spontaneous mutations. However, when the mutation rate per unit radiation dose was measured, it was found that the background radiation is too low by several orders of magnitude to account for the spontaneous rate. The experiments discussed here again demonstrate this.

The next idea was that these mutations are caused by an

error of replication of the DNA. Since many thousands, or even millions, of pieces of molecules must be replicated with perfect precision for each cell division, it would not be at all surprising if a few errors are made from time to time. However, the experiments discussed here show that, at least for the types of mutations discussed here, these mutations cannot primarily be due to errors of replication. The chromosome aberrations increase markedly in spite of the fact that there is no cell division.

Furthermore, this same thing has been observed when scoring true mutations in seeds. It has been found many times (see Sax, 1962) that when seeds are stored for several years the number of mutations increases dramatically. In this case there is also no cell division, but the cells develop mutations anyway.

The same conclusion was reached by Novick and Szilard (1950) working with bacteria in an apparatus they called a chemostat. By growing the cells in a calorie-deficient medium the division rate could be controlled over rather wide limits. By then testing for specific amino acid mutants, they found that the mutation rate was independent of the number of divisions, and depended only on the elapsed time. This indicates that even mutations involving an extremely small locus, the so-called point mutations, are not errors of replication.

Another piece of evidence indicates that mutations occur more readily in cells which divide rarely if at all. In a study of plants subjected to chronic gamma irradiation, Van't Hof and Sparrow (1963) found that for plants growing under conditions of continuous irradiation, the sensitivity of the plants depended markedly on the growing conditions of the plants. It developed that this was entirely a question of the rate of cell division. If the plants were growing very fast they could continue to grow in quite high radiation levels, but if they were growing slowly, relatively low radiation levels would stop growth or even kill some types of plants. Even when growth was slowed down by lowering the temperature, and keeping all other factors constant, this relationship prevailed. It turned out that they could predict the sensitivity of the plants by estimating the total amount of energy absorbed by the cells during any single division cycle.

In other words, radiation damage could be accumulated during one division cycle and if the damage was great enough, a lasting effect on the progeny of that cell was produced. If it was not this great, the slate was wiped clean and the daughter cells started as if there had been no previous radiation experience in that cell line.

This is essentially the same phenomenon as development of spontaneous mutations in cells which seldom undergo division. The cells behave as though quite a number of damaging events, generated either externally or internally, must take place in the chromosome structure of the cell, before the structure cannot repair the minor damage preparatory to replication. One can imagine many forms this damage could take in terms of bond breaking, etc. in the molecular structure of the chromosome, but most of this would be pure conjecture at the present time.

This, then, comes back to the recovery processes or repair mechanisms discussed earlier, and emphasizes again the need to understand cellular processes in molecular terms.

MUTATIONS IN DIFFERENT CELL TYPES

Within the mammal there is a wide variety of kinds of cells, and unquestionably each has its own susceptibility to both spontaneous and induced mutation. This susceptibility can take one of two forms. First, one can think of the inherent damage to the genetic structure of the somatic cell. One measure of this is the chromosomal aberrations discussed previously. The other facet of the susceptibility is in the amount of genetic damage a cell can suffer and still continue to function normally when it is not required to undergo division. A brain cell is very highly differentiated, so probably makes use of only a very small part of the genetic information contained within the cell. It seems reasonable to suppose then that these cells could suffer a great deal of damage to the genetic material (DNA) before, on the average, cellular function would be impaired. The two types of damage, then, are: (1) chromosomal rearrangements or damage to the anatomical structure of the nucleus, and (2) functional damage. Whereas there is probably never functional damage without structural damage, the converse is not necessarily true.

For the first type of damage there is a good deal of evidence to indicate that all the cells of a mammal are roughly equally sensitive. This conclusion comes from observations on the chromosomes of cells from a number of organs. The liver studies, previously discussed, showed that for a just sublethal dose of radiation, aberrations were visible in almost all cells immediately after the irradiation. Likewise, under the same condition, about the same percentage of cells of the bone marrow and intestinal epithelium showed chromosome aberrations. Oakberg (1961) has shown somewhat the same percentage in the spermatogonia. In all cells in which it has been possible to investigate chromosomal damage due to radiation, it is found to be about the same for all cell types.

Turning to the spontaneous chromosomal aberrations, the liver is the only organ in which they have been systematically studied. It has been shown by Steffensen (1955), however, that under a variety of conditions the same factors which lead to radiation sensitivity also lead to high spontaneous mutation rates and high percentages of chromosome aberrations in the plant *Tradescantia*. There is every reason to believe the same would be true of mammalian cells. It seems justified to conclude that the initial damage produced in the chromosomes, either spontaneously or radiation induced, is of about the same magnitude in all mammalian cells.

The consequences of this damage to the cell, the organ, and the individual vary enormously from one organ to another. First there is the recovery process which certainly operates on all cells, but there is virtually nothing known about the differences in this from one organ to another. Next there are the differences in the rate of cell division between the cells of various organs. The cells of the bone marrow divide at a high rate, but the brain cells of the adult never divide. Brain cells, for example, have the opportunity to heal themselves, as previously discussed, without having to undergo division. On the other hand, they will accumulate both radiation induced and spontaneous mutations which are too large to heal, and will have no opportunity to discard them by cell selection concomitant with cell division. If one examines the chromosome aberrations in liver cells some months after a dose of radiation, it is found that there are a great many aberrations in the cells of this organ. If the bone marrow is examined, however, it is found that practically all the induced aberrations have been eliminated by cell selection during cell division.

The next factor to be considered is the difference in function which the different cells perform irrespective of cell division. The highly differentiated cells probably make use of only a very small fraction of the genetic information contained in the chromosomes. It thus would be expected that such a cell could, on the average, suffer a great deal of chromosomal damage before a deficit of function would occur, and indeed this seems to be the case. A dose of radiation large enough to cause chromosome aberrations in virtually every cell of the liver, will still leave the liver well able to perform its normal function, and liver function tests show no deficit of physiological capability. In these circumstances, if one analyzes the liver for the content of specific enzymes, one finds the enzyme concentration within normal limits. One can go even further and induce production of enzymes normally found in the liver in only very small concentrations, and it is again found that enzyme induction is within normal values.

The brain can receive quite large doses of radiation with no apparent damage. When the brain is subjected to radiation doses large enough to cause visible damage, it is probably due not to primary damage to the nerve cells, but to damage to the endothelial cells of the blood capillaries. This was shown by a series of experiments with a deuteron microbeam (Zeman *et al.*, 1961). A beam of deuterons from a cyclotron could be regulated as to the beam diameter, and the dose of radiation delivered to the brain of a mouse accurately monitored. After varying periods of time the brains were examined histologically for damage. When the beam was 1 mm or more in diameter, extensive damage was caused by doses of about 10,000 rads, as predicted from clinical experience. However, when the beam diameter was reduced to 0.025 mm, the dose required to produce visible damage increased to as much as 400,000 rads. In other words, when a single nerve cell is irradiated without damage to surrounding supporting tissue, it can take a tremendous dose of radiation without visible damage even after 250 days. There must have been extensive damage to the genetic structure of these cells, and the only explanation which seems reasonable is that, since these cells do not undergo division, they need very little of their DNA for cellular function.

Applying these ideas to the aging problem, it is apparent that there are two distinct forces at work. First, if cells undergo division quite frequently, they will have little opportunity to acquire mutations, and even if they do acquire one, cell selection will probably eliminate it from the cell population after a very few cell divisions. Thus no increase in chromosome aberrations is seen in the bone marrow cells of aged mice, because they have all been eliminated by cell selection as soon as they appeared. These cells are immortal and do not exhibit aging, in the same sense and for the same reason that a culture of bacteria can be kept in an active state without growing "old" indefinitely. This is unquestionably the reason the embryo chicken heart cells kept in culture for so long by Carrell and Ebeling (1921) were able to escape aging. The rare exception to this rule is a mutation which confers a selective advantage on the daughter cells, and this is, in all probability, the start of a cancer. The mammalian cells which typify this type are bone marrow cells, gastric mucosal cells, epithelial cells, germ cells, etc.

If one does not include cancer as part of aging, one can say that these organs do not age. There seems to be excellent evidence to support such a statement. The blood functions well into extreme old age. Likewise, the gastrointestinal epithelium, the epidermis, etc., perform well, although the circulation to these organs may indirectly cause problems. It should be noted that the old appearance of the skin in old persons is due largely to the shrinkage of the connective tissue of the derma.

The second type of effect is found in the cells which seldom, if ever, undergo division in the adult. These cells have ample opportunity to undergo mutation, but, as discussed previously, an excellent opportunity to repair the genetic damage. Further, all such cells are highly differentiated and can sustain many mutations without impairing function. However, they have no opportunity to get rid of mutations which cannot be healed. These cells slowly accumulate mutations which eventually must reach the point where the cells either die or become very inefficient. This must be one of the mechanisms for the gradual loss of cells of the brain. Brody (1955) has estimated that there is a loss of more than 20 per cent of the brain cells in the human by the seventh decade of life; and many of the cells which do not die, probably function badly. The cells of this class do not become cancerous. Organs in this category include brain, muscle, kidney, pancreas, etc.

A few organs have cells intermediate between these two types, and the liver is a good example of this. Liver cells very seldom undergo division, but can be made to do so by the proper stimulus. The liver accumulates mutations, and does occasionally become cancerous.

These considerations make it apparent first, that aging is a cellular process and secondly, that the various cells in a mammal age differently and contribute in a multitude of ways to the aging of the total animal. Aging is a consequence of differentiation. In the mammal the genetic program takes the individual cells to a high state of differentiation and, so to speak, leaves them there. Since these cells cannot survive indefinitely, aging and death ultimately complete the program.

DELAYED EXPRESSION OF MUTATIONS

When one examines a mouse some weeks after a dose of radiation, it is very difficult, if not impossible, to say that anything is wrong with the animal. Even complex physiological tests such as liver or kidney function tests indicate that the animal has completely recovered. Blood counts have returned to normal. The age-specific death rate is essentially normal. Yet the life expectancy of the animal is much less than normal and when the liver cells are examined, it is found that the chromosomes may be grossly damaged in the vast majority of the cells, and such is undoubtedly true of a large fraction of all the cells of the body. One would almost be inclined to say that the aberrations do not cause the aging, because there is such a long lag between the production of the aberrations and their manifestation in terms of the shortening of the life span. There is no doubt that this presents a problem, but there is a ready explanation which can actually strengthen the concept of the mutation theory of aging.

The current concept of the role of the nucleus in the function of the somatic cell is that there is a specific DNA molecule in the chromosome complex for each cell function. This molecule synthesizes a corresponding RNA molecule which, in turn, synthesizes the specific protein, usually an enzyme, which catalyzes a reaction necessary for the function of the cell. If a single DNA molecule is damaged, it will ultimately abolish one enzyme system in the cell, and if this is essential to the function of the cell, it will eventually die. This may take some time, however, since it must first run out of all the corresponding protein and RNA molecules. It is quite conceivable that this time may be of the order of half the lifetime of the animal provided the cell does not have to undergo cell division. If the cell undergoes division, the RNA and protein will be divided equally between the daughter cells, and it is quite conceivable that there would be enough to carry on the normal function of both cells. If cell division took place several times, there is no doubt that the concentration would eventually get so low that the cells of that cell line would die.

This would certainly adequately explain the long delay between the production of the mutations and their expression, and it would be well to review the evidence both for and against this concept. First, it was observed many years ago that following a dose of radiation, cells continued to function normally until it came time to undergo division, and at that time the cell either died in the attempt or produced bizarre daughter cells which soon died. This is the response which underlies most reactions of living matter to ionizing radiation of moderate doses. One can easily imagine that a highly differentiated mammalian cell uses only a small fraction of its DNA to perform its functions, but when it undergoes division it must call on a great many more functions. If it is going to fail for the reason of DNA damage, by far the most probable time of failure will be at the time of cell division. This observation then fits the delayed expression idea very well.

Second, it was observed by Demerec (1946) that when mutations were produced in bacteria by x rays, the cells would continue to divide for as many as twelve times before the mutant character would express itself. Newcombe and Scott (1949) analyzed this phenomenon and concluded that the mutations were indeed induced at the time of the irradiation, but that they remained dormant for a number of cell divisions. This is known as phenotypic delay and has been verified many times since. The only reasonable explanation seems to be that the cells are functioning on their stored RNA and protein for a number of cell divisions.

Next, Puck (1961) grew mammalian cells in tissue culture, and observed that following x rays the cells could continue to divide for as many as four divisions, during which time they appeared quite normal. After this they formed bizarre daughter cells and eventually died. Here again it was apparent that the cells could continue to function and even divide quite normally for a relatively long time after severe chromosomal damage.

An extreme example of this was demonstrated some years ago by Harvey (1936) who centrifuged sea-urchin eggs into two halves, a nucleate and a non-nucleate half. The half lacking a nucleus continued to divide many times before the embryo disintegrated.

These experiments demonstrate that the control exercised by the nucleus can be considerably delayed, irrespective of the mechanisms of the delay. It would seem that the most obvious choice of the substance to be responsible for the delayed control would be RNA since it is known to be in the cytoplasm and to be responsible for the synthesis of proteins. However, most direct evidence seems to indicate that the turnover of RNA is quite rapid. Wulff *et al.* (1962, 1965) added labeled cytidine to the blood stream of mice and found that a good deal of it was incorporated into brain cells, as indicated by autoradiographic methods. Since cytidine is a normal constituent only of RNA, the inference is that even though there is no DNA synthesis in these cells, there is a continual RNA synthesis. This implies that an RNA molecule has only a relatively short life.

Studies by Brenner *et al.* (1961) on *Escherichia coli* also indicate that a single RNA molecule can synthesize only about four protein molecules before it disintegrates, which would require quite an active RNA turnover. Again Potter (1961) showed that induced enzymes of the liver are apparently induced in a day or two and disappear as fast. Other experiments also show a relatively rapid RNA turnover, which would tend to argue against explaining the delayed expression of mutations on this basis.

However, these experiments are far from disproving this concept. First, it should be pointed out that the incorporation of a labeled atom or even a labeled purine or pyrimidine, may not form an adequate label for RNA. The isotope may be merely involved in an exchange reaction, and may stick with the RNA molecule for a relatively short time. This idea appears quite a likely explanation following some recent experiments by Devik (1963). He injected labeled thymidine into rats and followed the uptake and decay of the label in liver cells by an autoradiographic technique. Normally the cells are quickly labeled and lose the label over a period of a very few days. This would indicate a rapid turnover of DNA in the liver where there is virtually no cell division. However, when he initiated cell division by a partial hepatectomy, and injected the labeled thymidine at the height of regeneration, quite a different picture was obtained. There was quite a rapid loss of part of the label as before, but there was also one component which had a very long decay, and, in fact, so long that it is questionable whether there was any decay over a period of many months. The obvious interpretation of this experiment is that if a DNA molecule is inactive, it can nevertheless engage in exchange reactions quite readily. However, if the label is firmly incorporated into the molecule as it can be during a true replication, then it is fixed and cannot be removed except by a true destruction of the molecule. These experiments were performed with DNA, but DNA and RNA are very similar from a molecular point of view. Applying these results to the RNA experiments just cited, the conclusion would seem to be that they were measuring, almost entirely, an exchange reaction. If this is true, they would have no bearing on the present problem. This would not apply to Potter's work with induced enzymes, but it is quite likely that this is a special case.

There are other possible mechanisms to explain the long delay between the production of a mutation and its expression. In diploid cells, in general, each cell function is represented twice, once on each homologous chromosome. If a mutation occurs to destroy one, the cell can continue to function with the other. In time, as spontaneous mutations build up in somatic cells, a mutation may occur in the other one and at this time the mutation will become apparent. This mechanism must function to at least some extent, but a rather simple experiment makes it appear not to account for any very large fraction of the observed effect. This experiment, which has been repeated a number of times (Jones and Kimmeldorf, 1964), consists in measuring the shortening of the life span in young *vs* old mice for a given dose of radiation. It is found that as the mice get older, the radiation has a decreasing effect on the life expectancy, until when the mice are quite old, the radiation seems to have no effect on the mortality rate. If aging were due to the production of two "hits" on homologous chromosomes, then the situation should be the reverse of the experiments just cited. One would expect an immediate effect on aging if the radiation were given to old mice. Since this is not the case, we must conclude that aging is not due to the production of "hits" on homologous chromosomes. The alternate explanation of the functioning of the cell on the stored RNA, discussed above, fits the experimental facts much better.

When a single dose of x rays is administered to an animal, the aberration frequency may rise to very high values and then decline over a period of many months (Fig. 11), so when the effect of this dose of radiation is starting to cause an increased mortality rate, the observed aberrations are about at the control levels. On the other hand, in the case of neutrons, there is no measurable recovery of the chromosome damage (Fig. 17). At the time the radiation dose is exerting its delayed effects, the radiation-induced chromosome aberrations bear no relation to the increased mortality rate. It would almost appear that this proves the chromosome aberrations are not responsible for the increased mortality rate. The fact remains, however, that there is a close correlation between the aberration frequency observed when the mouse is young and the mortality rate when the mouse is old. It would then seem that here again an explanation based on the very slow turnover of essential RNA and proteins is demanded. There seems little doubt that the chromosomal recovery observed is real in every sense of the word.

For gamma rays administered at a very low dose rate, there may be a 75 per cent chromosomal recovery within a few hours, and this recovery is effective in preventing a shortening of the life span. For example, a dose of 2000 rads of gamma rays to mice, administered very slowly, will cause about as many aberrations and also about the same radiation-induced aging as an acute dose of gamma rays of 500 rads. About the same effect will be produced by 250 rads of neutrons. The aberrations produced by the gamma rays will decline steadily, but those produced by neutrons will not. Yet whether they decline or not, will make no difference as far as the induced aging is concerned.

Two possible explanations come to mind to account for this apparent contradiction. The first is the very real possibility that the chromosome aberrations are only an external manifestation of point mutations which are not visible in the microscope, but are, nevertheless, the entities causing the malfunction. On this basis it is quite possible that the aberrations may heal but leave the point mutations unaffected. The other possibility is that the normal feed-back mechanisms of the cell which keep it functioning smoothly become so badly disrupted by the long delay between the production of an aberration and its final healing, that the cell cannot get back in harmony again. It is well to remember at this point that radiation delivered to an old animal produces many aberrations but no shortening of the life span, demonstrating again that the number of aberrations present when the animal is old does not affect his life span. Even though the explanation for this is not known, it does not necessarily argue against the mutation theory of aging.

THE SOMATIC MUTATION RATE

It is quite impossible to judge from these studies the actual mutation rate in these somatic cells. Indeed, it raises the question as to what is meant by the mutation rate in a somatic cell. Clearly if a change in the genome of the cell were to take place conferring a changed character (e.g., a biochemical deficiency) on the progeny, then one would be justified in saying that a somatic mutation had taken place. If, however, a cell suffers a break in a chromosome in the resting cell, and the cell is never required to undergo division, can one say a mutation has occurred? All the genetic information is still present in the cell, and there is at least some evidence to indicate that the cell can still function perfectly. There are such phenomena as position effects and genetic balance which undoubtedly influence the behavior of the cell, but there is no real evidence as to the role of these effects in a mammalian somatic cell.

Even taking these effects into consideration, it would seem almost out of the question to think of a cell which appears grossly abnormal in its chromosome behavior during cell division as being genetically normal. It would seem safe to state dogmatically that such a cell has a multitude of mutations.

If this is true, how does one reconcile the very high spontaneous mutation rate in somatic cells with the very low mutation rate as measured in the germ cells by standard genetic methods? Either the germ cells have very much lower mutation rates, or the process of maturation and fertilization constitute a very effective screening mechanism permitting only the perfect, or nearly perfect, cells to get through to produce offspring. Substantiating the latter is the work of Oakberg and Clark

(1961) who observed the oocytes and spermatogonia in mice following irradiation. Even after a very small dose of radiation there was considerable chromosomal damage, perhaps even more than one would see in liver cells after a comparable dose. But if Oakberg and Clark waited a few weeks, they could see nothing. It seems reasonable to conclude that most of the defective cells are eliminated by cell division, and practically all the rest of the defective cells are incapable of producing fertilization. Only a very occasional minor mutation will slip through.

One of the primary objections to the somatic mutation theory has been that the mutation rate, as computed from the known genetic mutation rate, is much too low to account for the known facts of aging. These recent experiments effectively remove this objection.

It is interesting to speculate on the teliological consequences of these ideas. There is no doubt that death is a tragedy for the individual, but a moment's reflection will convince one that it is a necessity for the survival of the species. Evolution requires a continual turnover of individuals, so the old ones must die in order to make way for the new. Mutation is necessary to produce the gradual change in the germ plasm responsible for the origins of new species. It now appears that mutations are also responsible for the aging and eventual death of individuals.

CORRELATIONS

There are, by now, many pieces of information which fit very nicely with the ideas of the mutation theory of aging. It has been known for many years that, in both mice and men, the offspring of old mothers have more inborn defects and a shorter life span than those of young mothers (Jacobs *et al.*, 1959). If the age of the father has any influence in this regard, it must be very small. For example, it is known that mongolism is due to a genetic defect, and occurs many times more frequently in the offspring of mothers over forty years old than in those of young mothers (Penrose, 1961). It would seem very attractive to postulate, following the evidence presented above, that since the oocytes in the female stay in the ovary for a long time without undergoing cell division, they can accumulate mutations as time goes on, some of which can survive meiosis to endow the offspring with mutations. The spermatogonia are continually undergoing division and would tend to eliminate any mutations by cell selection.

There is also abundant evidence indicating that the longer the time lag between maturation and fertilization for germ cells, the greater the number of mutations will be developed. It was shown by Dungay (1913) that *Arbacia* sperm, when kept for some hours after shedding, not only had a lower fertility, but of the viable fertilizations that did take place, there were many more developmental abnormalities than in sperm used at once.

Byers and Muller (1952) allowed *Drosophila* spermatozoa to age in the female spermotheca at either 7° or 27° C for periods up to three weeks. In all cases the mutation rate was higher the longer the storage period. Also, for any given storage period, the mutation rate was much higher for the higher temperatures.

A good deal of work has been done on this problem in connection with artificial insemination. For example, Salisbury *et al.* (1962) estimated the mutation rate for bull sperm kept at 5° C over a period of five days. The fertility rate decreased steadily over this period from about 80 per cent to about 60 per cent, while the calving rate decreased from about 70 per cent to about 45 per cent. The authors interpreted the difference between the two curves to represent the lethal mutation rate, which thus increased with the age of the sperm. When the sperm was kept at −79° C, the same phenomenon was observed but the change took place over a period of months rather than days.

The same is true for aging of the ovum. Young and Blandau (1939) found that female guinea pigs, inseminated at different times after ovulation (a few hours at most), show a decreased fertility and increased number of abnormal embryos as the time increased.

The development of mutations in germ cells over these short periods of time may not seem to represent the same phenomenon as that related to the development of mutations in somatic cells, which apparently takes place over a period of years at 37° C in the human. However, it is not difficult to think of the two as being different aspects of the same phenomenon. The germ cells are composed almost entirely of DNA, and endowed with enough enzymes and stores of energy to last for a very short period of time. The mechanisms responsible for the stability of the chromosome structure are probably poorly developed. Further, they are haploid cells, which means that if a chromosome break occurred, there would be no homologous chromosome present to act as a template for its repair.

In any event, whereas these facts do not add direct substantiation to the mutation theory of aging, they correlate with the ideas of that theory very well by showing that in other biological systems mutations take place with time, and the mutations have serious consequences for the function of the cell.

THE RATE OF LIVING THEORY

It was indicated above, that, although the rate of living theory does not have any real proof to substantiate it, enough pieces of evidence suggest its validity that one hesitates to discard it. It can now be seen that this concept fits well with the somatic mutation theory. There must be a long lag between the production of a mutation and its manifestation in terms of cell function, and during this time the cell is functioning by means of its stored RNA and proteins. If the proteins are being used up faster by an increased metabolism, any mutation affecting the genes involved in metabolism will make its deficiency felt sooner. The aging would be started by mutations, and once started, could be accelerated by an increased metabolism. On this basis it would seem that there is no conflict whatever between these two theories.

In subsequent chapters it will be shown that some aging phenomena are not at all susceptible to explanation purely in terms of the mutation theory, but when this rate of living concept is added, the combination fits the facts remarkably well.

AGING IN TISSUE CULTURE

Mammalian cells can now be grown in tissue culture, and

although the cells are probably not in a completely optimal situation, we can still learn a great deal about the aging of cells from such studies. It was found that the cells of a small bit of tissue, taken from animals under sterile conditions and cultured according to the techniques of Puck (1961), may start to grow, after a short latent period, and increase logarithmically for a certain length of time. The growth then levels off in spite of the fact that the cells are continually being transferred to fresh medium. Following this, there is a period of decline and death. Occasionally, a change in the culture takes place which seems to correspond to a tumor, in which case these new cells continue to grow indefinitely like a culture of bacteria.

Ignoring this cancer-like growth, normal cells seem to go through a certain number of cell divisions in culture and then go to pieces. In practically all these cultures, irrespective of what kind of cells were used for the starting material, the fibroblasts predominate after a few transfers, and the more highly differentiated cells disappear. There is at least some evidence to indicate that the other cells, e.g., epithelial cells, disappear because they can only go through very few cell divisions before becoming "old" and dying off. It is not technically possible to culture a pure specimen of one kind of cell. Every tissue sample contains at least a few fibroblasts and these soon take over the culture.

Assuming, however, that all mammalian cells would go through the same sequence as do fibroblasts, some interesting correlations seem reasonable. First, the concept of a limited number of cell divisions for highly differentiated cells is quite consistent with the mutation hypothesis and also the rate of living idea. Further, Hayflick (1965) observed that as the cells reached the final stage of the culture, the number of abnormalties seen in the chromosomes increased very considerably. Finally, there is even some indication from his work that cells taken from a young individual will go through more cell divisions before they stop dividing than cells from an old individual.

It is interesting to note in this connection that much the same phenomenon has been observed when mammalian cells are cultured *in vivo*. Krohn (1963) transplanted skin from an old mouse to a genetically identical young one, and when that mouse became old, transferred the same piece of skin to another young mouse, etc. He found that this process was successful in keeping the skin alive and healthy to only a very limited extent. In spite of the fact that the grafts seemed to "take" perfectly, the skin could be kept alive only a little longer than the normal skin of a mouse.

These experiments lend great support to the general concept of the mutation theory as developed in this chapter. They also serve to emphasize the importance of cellular aging in the process of senescence, and to indicate that the act of differentiation has somehow deprived the individual cell of the potential of unlimited cell division which it originally possessed.

AN AGING HORMONE

It has often been postulated that the endocrine glands play a dominant role in aging. There is no doubt whatever that they are largely responsible for the regulation of the developmental process associated with growth, maturation, reproduction, etc., and it would seem not unreasonable to think of them as responsible for the completion of the cycle by regulating aging. In spite of intensive search, no such regulation has ever been established. The old practice of trying to restore youth by various forms of hormones has uniformly failed.

However, it has been pointed out that the mutation rate in somatic cells is very high in the mammal. From work with plants it is known that a number of factors affect the mutation rate. A change in the calcium ion concentration of the growth medium can make a difference of a factor of ten in the spontaneous mutation rate (Steffensen, 1955). Other ions are also effective. Many mutagenic chemicals are now known which can cause a profound change in mutation rate, but none of them is a natural product. However, such a natural compound probably does exist. Evidence for this comes from the work of Demerec (1937) who showed that certain genes in *Drosophila* were responsible for a large change in the spontaneous mutation rate.

These are called mutator genes and have subsequently been found in microorganisms and plants as well. They behave as though they were responsible for the synthesis within the cell of a substance which could diffuse to the other parts of the nucleus and cause mutations in other genes. Indeed it is difficult to understand how this gene could function except by some mechanism such as this, but the substance has not been isolated.

From these possibilities it is evident that the spontaneous mutation rate for any group of cells is not an invariant fixed quantity, but can vary considerably depending on both internal and external variables. Accordingly one can think of two possible explanations for the very high somatic mutation rate. The first would be that the final step in differentiation would uncover a mutator gene which would cause a high mutation rate and thus eventually cause the death of the organism. The second would be that one of the endocrine glands would secrete a hormone which was mutagenic, thus ensuring a high mutation rate.

These are only vague possibilities, which have virtually no foundation in experimental fact, but do indicate that one should keep an open mind in such matters. They also give great hope for the future, since it appears that the only method of drastically prolonging the life span of man lies in understanding and rectifying the mutation process.

SUMMARY

Evidence primarily from studies on chromosome aberrations in mice and comparisons between natural and radiation-induced aging have shown a close correlation between the production of chromosome aberrations (mutations) and aging. These studies give great support to the somatic mutation theory of aging, but show it must be modified in at least two important regards. First, there is a long time lag between mutation production and its ultimate effect on aging; so only the mutations produced while the animal is relatively young are effective in shortening the life span. Next, during this time lag the cells are existing on previously synthesized components (RNA and proteins), so to some extent the duration of life will depend on the utilization of these components (rate of living). Also, mutations may be very important in aging in some forms (mammals), but are probably of minor importance in others (plants). By means of these ideas a great many experimental facts regarding aging may be correlated.

Chapter 5

AGING IN MAMMALS

THE COMPLEXITY OF THE PROBLEM

IN THE foregoing chapters the various theories of senescence have been discussed as if there were one all-embracing theory which would explain all the known phenomena which have come to be associated with aging. This would almost be like asking for a single all-embracing theory to explain all of mammalian physiology. The entire process of senescence is unquestionably extremely complex, and the factors leading to the manifestations of aging in one organ are almost certainly different from those in another. In reviewing the various theories of aging it appears that the somatic mutation theory has the most to recommend it at the present time. The questions then arise: How do the accumulating mutations in the cells of the body lead to the known signs and symptoms of aging? How do they lead to the various degenerative diseases? Factors other than somatic mutations must play some part in the aging phenomenon—where do they fit in the picture? At the present time much of the discussion of these questions must be speculative, but it is based on a certain amount of substantial information which gives some excellent guideposts (Curtis, 1963b).

It is beyond the scope of this monograph to discuss all the signs and symptoms of aging in the light of the various theories of aging. In the last chapter it was pointed out that the individual cells develop chromosomal aberrations (mutations) which are highly correlated with senescence. It is then not surprising to find that many histological and biochemical changes are seen in the cells of organs taken from old animals. Each organ has its own characteristic cellular changes, and while it is not now

84

possible to correlate directly the chromosomal changes with the histological or biochemical changes, one is justified in saying that, with the large degree of chromosomal damage present, it would be surprising if there were not many consequent cellular changes. Such effects have been adequately described elsewhere (Lansing, 1952; Korenchevsky, 1961). However, there are a number of generalizations which apply with greater or lesser force to all organ systems, and these will be discussed here.

It should be emphasized again that the aging process is one which leads to degeneration simultaneously on many fronts. Attention is again directed to Figures 1 and 3 which show that in spite of recent phenomenal advances in medical science, the maximum life span of man has hardly been lengthened at all. Thus, if a person contracts cancer, for example, at age forty the probability of a cure with proper medical care may be very good, whereas the same form of cancer in a person of seventy-five may be almost invariably fatal in spite of the best of modern medical care. Dublin *et al.* (1949) have shown this very dramatically by demonstrating, from actuarial data, that if all cancer were to be eliminated from the human population, the average life span of persons in the United States would be lengthened by only 1.5 years. The reason, of course, lies in the fact that the death rate from all causes increases exponentially with age. So if an old person were spared from one disease, another would cause his demise very soon. This demonstrates again the nonspecific nature of senescence, and the futility of trying to describe senescence in terms of the disease entities by which senescence is usually manifested.

CANCER INDUCTION

Cancer is usually considered, and rightly so, as one of the degenerative processes associated with aging, so it must be considered as one of the facets of the total problem. There have been countless theories put forward to explain cancer induction, but one which seems to fit much of the more recent experimental evidence is the two-factor theory as discussed principally by Berenblum (1963). Briefly, an initiator and a promoter are both

required to produce a cancer. A number of substances and conditions can be found which will produce one or the other of these
factors. For example, one of the most potent initiators for skin
cancer in the mouse is urethane, and the most effective promoting agent is croton oil. Urethane alone is not carcinogenic
and croton oil is only slightly carcinogenic if applied for a long
time. Tumors appear in large numbers if the promoting agent
follows the application of the initiating agent, but not the reverse.
Some substances such as benzpyrene can act as both initiator
and promoter since they are not carcinogenic when applied once,
but are very carcinogenic if applied repeatedly at appropriate
intervals.

The evidence lends itself to the interpretation that the initiator
must be something which either causes a mutation or "uncovers"
a site on the genetic structure of the cell which in the normal
animal is covered. To explain this last statement it is necessary
to consider recent ideas concerning differentiation. These concepts, for which there is a good deal of experimental evidence,
postulate that a cell undergoes differentiation by covering up
part of its DNA or otherwise inactivating it, so some cellular
functions are suppressed and others are accentuated. Even in
the very highly differentiated cells, however, all the genetic
information is still present. One very plausible explanation is
that there are specific proteins (histones) which combine with
specific sites (DNA molecules) on the genome. Dedifferentiation
would then take place when one or more of these sites were
uncovered by removal of the appropriate blocking protein. It is
impossible at the present time to distinguish between mutation
and dedifferentiation in cancer induction, and it is quite possible
that some cancers are produced in one way and others in the
other.

The evidence further is consistent with the idea that the
promoting agent is one which produces a stimulus for cell
division. The mutated cell then is forced into cell division, and
since it does not respond to the influences which limit the size
of the normal organ, a neoplasm results.

According to this concept, it is easy to see why radiation is a potent carcinogenic agent since it is such an excellent mutagen. A number of recent experiments substantiate this picture; perhaps the most definite is by Cole and Nowell (1964). They irradiated mice with neutrons when the mice were young and examined them for hepatomas when the mice were quite old. In addition, some of the irradiated mice were subsequently given single injections of CCl_4 which destroys part of the liver, causing a rapid regeneration. Normal mice and those receiving a dose of CCl_4 exhibited only about 2 per cent hepatomas; those receiving radiation alone, about 19 per cent; and those receiving radiation followed by CCl_4, about 61 per cent. Neutrons are known to produce many mutations in the liver, and CCl_4 is known to give a very powerful stimulus for cell division.

It would appear that in the normal aging process somatic mutations occur which set the stage for neoplasia. At some later time something gives the proper stimulus for cell division and the process of neoplasia starts. Irritation of a tissue, which certainly gives a stimulus for cell division, is a very common cause of cancer.

One of the most vigorous arguments against the mutation concept of carcinogenesis is that mutation is usually considered a rather rare event, and when the conditions are correct for cancer induction, it will occur in several sites simultaneously. Thus in a heavy cigarette smoker who contracts bronchial cancer, a pathologic examination shows that there usually have been several independent sites of origin. However, the current work (Chapter 4) shows that mutation is a very common event. One could think that in a tissue such as the bronchial epithelium in which the cells undergo division rather slowly, mutations accumulate slowly over a period of years. Then, when the appropriate promoter is introduced, such as the irritation to the bronchus of cigarette smoking, the conditions conducive to cancer formation are present and its eventual realization becomes a virtual certainty.

From this discussion it might be supposed that organs which are continually in active cell division would always be ripe for cancer induction. However, one must remember that in a tissue such as this, if a mutation is formed, there is a high probability of its being eliminated by cell selection. Also, as previously mentioned, there is evidence to indicate that the mutation rate may actually be lower in cells in active division because the cell spends less time in interphase where the chromosome instabilities seem to develop.

For these reasons it would seem that for rapidly dividing tissue, a promoter is continually present, forcing cell division and the initiator (mutations) are the limiting factor. In other tissues, in which cell division is quite slow, the initiator is present in the form of abundant mutations especially as the tissue ages, but the promoter is the limiting factor.

It appears that one of the commonest consequences of aging fits very nicely with the general concepts of the somatic mutation theory of aging.

There is abundant evidence indicating that viruses and other similar agents play a very large part in the etiology of many cancers. There is also at least some evidence indicating that particles which have usually been called viruses may be created in the individual at the time of cancer induction (Wald *et al.*, 1964). There is then some question as to just what a virus is and just what a mutation is. The clarification of these questions must await further research.

AUTOIMMUNE DISEASES

One of the most delicate of mammalian cell functions is the immune reaction, by which a cell recognizes as "foreign" every other cell which is not genetically identical. Even very minor genetic differences can be recognized in this way, and it is now thought that there is a large class of diseases, known as autoimmune diseases, which are caused by minor histocompatibility differences in the cells of one individual. Among such diseases are arthritis, arteriosclerosis, scleroderma, and even progeria.

Walford (1962) has presented a very good case for the idea that spontaneous mutations occur in various cells of the body in weak histocompatibility loci, thereby creating some cells in the body only slightly different from the rest in their immunologic characteristics. If a mutation occurred creating a very strong immunologic difference, it would be immediately eliminated.

A weak histocompatibility difference is by far the most probable change to be expected. Consider that the somatic cells, for a particular immunity character, have a genetic constitution represented by Aa. The normal progeny of these cells would, of course, also have the Aa genes, but if a mutation occurred it would probably affect only one of the homologous chromosomes, and cause either the change A→a or a→A. In this case the daughter cells would have a genetic constitution of AA or aa. In either case the same genetic characters will be present in the cell, but they will have a different balance. Thus the normal Aa cell would not necessarily recognize one of these mutant cells as being very different, and would not react strongly to it. Yet there is a substantial body of evidence to indicate that differences at weak histocompatibility loci will eventually lead to the auto-immune diseases and a shortening of the life span. This would then be one of the ways in which somatic mutations would lead to aging, and the evidence favoring this view will be briefly reviewed.

There is at least some evidence that there is an increase in the average immunological reaction in humans as they grow older. The gamma globulins, which are the blood proteins responsible for immunologic reactions, increase steadily with age (Das, 1961). The spleen is one of the important organs responsible for the manufacture of the gamma globulins and is always enlarged when chronic immunologic reactions are present. The average spleen weight relative to the body weight increases steadily with age in man (Walford and Hildemann, 1964). Studies on the effect of age on the "takes" of skin grafts between mice having minor histocompatibility differences were very revealing (see Walford, 1962). When the mice were quite young there were about 75 per cent successful grafts, but this decreased steadily until no grafts were successful when old mice were used as both donor and recipient. Whereas there may be other factors at work in this experiment, it certainly points to a situation of "immunologic diversification," to quote Walford. In other words, as the animals grew older they developed more and more minor immunologic differences as a result of somatic mutations which made it increasingly difficult to effect a successful skin graft.

There is also some evidence that increasing the numbers of minor histocompatibility differences by artificial means will speed the aging process. It is well known that if F_1 hybrids from two inbred strains of mice are injected neonatally with parental lymphoid cells, splenomegaly will result. The same is true of young mice injected with lymphoid cells from mice of a very closely similar, but not identical, inbred strain. These mice suffer a shortening of the life span and tend to die of a wide variety of degenerative diseases. The same is true of hamsters made parabiotic (Walford and Hildemann, 1964). They seem to have a considerably reduced life expectancy and die prematurely of degenerative diseases. They also develop amyloidosis at an early age, a condition almost invariably associated with old age in this animal. Significantly, Blumenthal and Berns (1965) have shown that patients with diabetes have antibodies circulating in the blood which are specifically directed against the individual's own insulin-producing cells. Diabetes, therefore, may well be classed as an autoimmune disease.

There seems to be no doubt that amyloidosis is the direct result of an immunologic reaction. It has long been known that in some animals the amyloid builds up in almost all organs of the body, and this leads to their malfunction. For example, when such a reaction takes place in the kidney, the glomeruli become clogged with this material and finally nonfunctional. When the kidney tubule cells are attacked, the reaction tends to block the nephron. If the reaction is with an endothelial cell of a blood capillary, that capillary becomes blocked. The amyloid is deposited in the brain, and probably leads to malfunction there.

It used to be felt that man was rather resistant to the deposition of amyloid. However, more recent histological methods have been developed which are quite specific for the identification of amyloid. Using these methods it has been shown that these deposits can be quite common in man, and extensive enough in one individual to cause serious malfunction. It is interesting to note that radiation accelerates the appearance of amyloid deposits in animals.

This evidence is far from conclusive, but it points rather strongly to the possibility that somatic mutations lead to minor histocompatibility differences which gradually may bring on one or another of the autoimmune diseases.

GENERALIZED AGING

Generalized aging means the sort of vicious circle which can be achieved in a complex mechanism, such as a mammal, when one part gets out of step with the others. For example, the heart muscle can become somewhat weakened, which tends to lower the blood pressure, which in turn causes a stimulus to the heart which further weakens it. Homeostatic forces attempt to keep the individual functioning in perfect condition and in wild animals this is very necessary. There it is do-or-die, and it is thus necessary to keep the individual in perfect working condition at all costs as long as possible. In a modern human society these homeostatic forces sometimes act against the well-being of the individual, and much of modern medical treatment in this area is designed to combat these forces. Modern drugs work to keep the blood pressure down, to decrease mental alertness, to relax muscle tone, etc.

It has long been felt that the collagen diseases are prime suspects in the search for "the" cause of aging. The more modern view would be that these diseases are certainly present in the aging individual but they are probably not directly due to a faulty collagen metabolism *per se* (Sinex, 1960). As discussed previously, somatic mutations probably induce weak histocompatability reactions which may lead to these disease states. On the other hand, a somatic mutation in an organ like the dermis may produce the death of a cell which will leave behind it a strand of collagen. As time goes on, the collagen tends to shrink, giving the wrinkled appearance to old skin. At the same time, it chokes off blood capillaries leaving a small area somewhat anoxic. This anoxia tends to encourage the death of more cells, and so it goes. In addition, this situation provides an excellent environment for the development of cancer, and in this sense acts as a promoting agent. The formation of cancers at the edge of old scars is a well known phenomenon. Generalized arteriosclerosis leads to a sequence of events too well known to repeat here.

It is well known that diseases for which there is very little acquired immunity, like pneumonia, increase in frequency and severity exponentially with age in the same way as do the degenerative diseases. Somatic mutations certainly do not cause such diseases, but from this discussion it is easy to see how an individual's resistance to such diseases would be broken down as a consequence of the effect of mutations on the various organs of the body.

Atherosclerosis is a disease characterized by an abnormal cholesterol metabolism in the large arteries. Werthessen (1962) found that if an atherosclerotic plaque from an artery is cultured, there are very distinctive and different biochemical pathways of cholesterol metabolism. When the progeny of these cells are subcultured it is again found that these cells continue to show the altered metabolism. When normal arterial cells are grown in culture, and subcultured, one always finds a normal metabolism. In other words, it appears that a mutation occurred in one or more cells in the atherosclerotic arterial wall which changed the metabolism of the cell to give it a selective advantage for survival, or at least no selective disadvantage. However, the arterial wall formed by these mutated cells is not quite as stable as the normal wall, and occasionally pieces break off causing disasterous consequences for the individual. This concept is far from proven, but it fits the known facts too well to be ignored.

These examples show a few of the manifestations of the process of senescence. In any one individual as he ages, many such degenerative processes proceed simultaneously, adding to the complexity of the problem. The disease which finally causes the demise in a very old person is largely a matter of chance, since a multitude of malfunctions exist by that time and if one is avoided another will soon dominate.

Thus we return to the thesis that aging in a mammal is a very complex phenomenon and while it unquestionably has its origins in basic cellular reactions, the complete description of the process must necessarily be very intricate.

CELLULAR METABOLISM

Rubner (1908) advanced the idea that each mammal is endowed with a certain metabolic capacity, and when this is used up, death ensues. He measured the heat output of a number of animals and found a remarkable correlation between the rate of heat output per gram of animal and its life span (see Chap. 2). Pearl (1928) and others have jumped to the conclusion that if the metabolism is speeded up, the life span will thereby be shortened. As previously pointed out, Rubner's observation may be merely an interesting correlation, and Pearl was unable to substantiate his ideas experimentally except in special cases. However, there is too much evidence favoring the idea to ignore it.

It was pointed out in Chapter 4 that it is necessary to postulate that a mammalian cell can function for a long time with damaged DNA, using the stored RNA for protein synthesis. Indeed there is at least some evidence to indicate that at the time cells differentiate to form their final cell type in an organism, they are endowed with their full complement of RNA, and no further RNA is made until the cell undergoes division. Jacobson (1951) employed histochemical staining methods to distinguish between DNA and RNA in mouse liver cells. He found almost no RNA in interphase nuclei. As the nuclear membrane started to break down in mitosis, RNA appeared associated with DNA. It continued to increase in amount and then decreased to zero at the formation of the nuclear membrane in telophase. It appeared that RNA was synthesized only during cell division.

If this is true, and if, as seems highly likely, the RNA and proteins are used up during metabolism, then a cell will have a finite lifetime dependent on the cellular metabolism. If the cells can undergo division, they can rejuvenate themselves. This would form a logical explanation for the postulates of Rubner and

Pearl and at the same time fit nicely with the other mechanisms of aging already discussed.

The experiments of Johnson *et al.* (1961) and Carlson (1957) showed that rats, kept at a cold temperature so the metabolism had to be increased in order to maintain body temperature, had a shorter life span. This certainly argues in favor of the metabolism idea. The shrew, who eats very large amounts of food and has a very high metabolism, has a short life span. The pocket mouse continually undergoes a form of hibernation in which the metabolism drops very low, and has a very long life span.

It is difficult to know how to classify the animals kept on a restricted diet whose life span may be very markedly increased thereby (McCay *et al.*, 1943; Berg and Simms, 1961) (Fig. 19). The metabolism per gram of tissue is virtually unchanged from the unrestricted animal. However, the over-all energy metabolism of the unrestricted animal is considerably higher. If one accepts the latter explanation it would seem to fit the general pattern, but the explanation offered in terms of reserve RNA would no

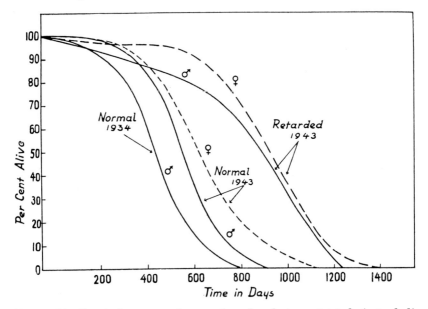

Figure 19. Survival curves of normal and calorie restricted (retarded) rats (from McCay, Sperling and Barnes, 1943).

longer be tenable. In view of these uncertainties it would seem wiser at the present time to admit that we do not know why these animals live longer, and reserve judgment until more is known about them.

It would seem fair to say that metabolism does play a role in aging, and that differentiated cells may use up their available supply of some vital substances, probably RNA, and thereby bring on the symptoms of senescence. However, in the human, other factors come into play and it seems highly probable that the beneficial effects of exercise outweight the deleterious effects of the increased metabolism.

GENETIC FACTORS

It is a well known truism that in order to live a long and healthy life one should choose parents and grandparents who were healthy and long-lived. Indeed there is excellent evidence to substantiate this claim. One can see this especially in different inbred strains of mice which differ in their median life spans by more than a factor of two. It will be well to inquire briefly concerning the reasons for these great differences in longevity between apparently closely similar strains of animals. Is there some one character common to short-lived or long-lived strains which confers this difference?

Many conditions commonly associated with aging, such as cataracts, greying of the hair, wrinkling of the skin, etc., are seen in young animals in many inbred lines of mice which are quite long-lived. These common accompaniments of aging are apparently quite superficial and are not necessarily symptomatic of an underlying senescence. Everyone is familiar with persons who are prematurely grey or bald, but who live long and healthy lives.

When the causes of death of short-lived strains of mice are examined, it is often found that a genetic trait makes them prone to the development of some particular disease at an early age. One strain regularly develops leukemia, another lung cancer, another nephrosclerosis, etc. In addition to strains which have a genetic character conferring a particular disease, some strains are relatively short-lived and it is found that they die of a wide spectrum of disease. In other words, it appears that the generalized aging process is accelerated in these strains, and it was one such strain which was compared, in Chapter 4, to a long-lived strain.

Gowan (1962) made a study of the various genetic factors responsible for aging. In one study he compares the genetic characteristics in mice which make up their resistance or susceptibility to *Salmonella*. With only very minor genetic differences between strains, some show very mild symptoms, and others die. When one infects these mice with different strains of *Salmonella* one again obtains a somewhat different picture. With just two genetic variables it is possible to get a very great diversity of response. This and an abundance of other evidence indicates that genetic factors play a dominant, though very complex, role in susceptibility to disease.

Gowan (1962) has also shown that the usual laws of genetic inheritance do not, in general, apply to the aging problem. For example, in the case of animals whose parents had genetic characters designated by AA^1, one would expect three phenotypes, AA, AA^1 and A^1A^1. In certain cases either the AA or A^1A^1 was found to be missing and on examination it was found that this combination resulted in embryos which died *in utero* or soon thereafter. In other cases a particular phenotype could be shown to be short-lived. In other words, it is not only a question of the particular genetic inheritance of an individual, but the balance between the different characters which determine whether the individual will have a high or a low probability of longevity.

Aging is itself a very complex reaction, and genetic factors which control such functions as disease resistance, cancer susceptibility, etc. undoubtedly react among themselves to produce a very profound influence on aging. One of the most convincing arguments indicating the importance of the interactions of genetic characters is the fact that identical twins live to very nearly the same age, whereas the age at death of the general population varies widely.

ENVIRONMENTAL FACTORS

In human aging, the life span is determined not only by the mechanisms of aging just discussed, but by a host of environmental factors as well. Some of these, like the communicable diseases, hardly seem a part of the aging picture even though they do sometimes drastically shorten the life span of populations. On the other hand, aging certainly alters the susceptibility to disease. Other factors, such as air pollution of cities and cigarette smoking, play an important role in determining life span. It has only recently been recognized that total food consumption is an important variable, and it is likely that specific foods will be found to play their parts, although none have been conclusively proven yet. The environmental factors, while not themselves to be considered mechanisms of aging, help form the groundwork by which the mechanisms are expressed.

It is interesting to note the magnitude of some of these environmental and hereditary factors, and these have been compiled by Jones (1960) (Table II). Communicable disease factors, which can play a dramatic role, have been omitted from consideration both because they are difficult to quantify and because they play a relatively small part in western societies.

From this table it is seen that in the western human population of today some of the environmental factors can be as important as the genetic or disease factors in determining the longevity of the individual.

SUMMARY

In mammals the mutation theory of aging, with the concomitant rate of living theory, fits the known facts reasonably well. Mutations in somatic cells lead to the manifestations of senescence in various ways. A mutation in a cell, combined with a stimulus for cell division, may lead to cancer. It may also cause minor histocompatability differences leading to the development of one of the autoimmune diseases. Atherosclerosis may be due to a mutation leading to a changed cholesterol metabolism; and vascular damage may be due to mutations induced in capillary endothelial cells. The life span of an indi-

TABLE II

PHYSIOLOGICAL AGE AND LIFE-SPAN DIFFERENCES (FROM JONES, 1960)

Reversible		Permanent	
Comparison	Years	Comparison	Years
Country versus city dwelling	+ 5	Female versus male sex..........	+ 3
Married status versus single, widowed, divorced..............	+ 5	Familial constitutions	
Overweight		2 grandparents lived to 80 years	+ 2
25 per cent overweight group	− 3.6	4 grandparents lived to 80 years	+ 4
35 per cent overweight group	− 4.3	Mother lived to age 90 yr.	+ 3
45 per cent overweight group	− 6.6	Father lived to age 90 yr.	+ 4.4
55 per cent overweight group	−11.4	Both mother and father lived to age 90 years......	+ 7.4
67 per cent overweight group	−15.1	Mother lived to age 80 years............................	+ 1.5
Or: an average effect of 1 per cent overweight........	− 0.17	Father lived to age 80 years	+ 2.2
Smoking		Both mother and father lived to age 80 years....................	+ 3.7
1 package cigarettes per day	− 7	Mother died at 60 years......	− 0.7
2 packages cigarettes per day	−12	Father died at 60 years......	− 1.1
Atherosclerosis		Both mother and father died at age 60 years......	− 1.8
Fat metabolism		Recession of childhood and infectious disease over past century in Western countries	+15
In 25th percentile of population having "ideal" lipoprotein concentrations	+10	Life Insurance Impairment Study	
Having average lipoprotein concentrations......	0	Rheumatic heart disease, evidenced by:	
In 25th percentile of population having elevated lipoproteins........	− 7	Heart murmur........................	−11
		Heart murmur + tonsillitis....	−18
In 5th percentile of population having highest elevation of lipoproteins	−15	Heart murmur + streptococcal infection....................	−13
		Rapid pulse............................	− 3.5
Diabetes		Phlebitis	− 3.5
Uncontrolled, before insulin, 1900......................	−35	Varicose veins.......................	− 0.2
		Epilepsy	−20.0
Controlled with insulin		Skull fracture........................	− 2.9
1920 Joslin Clinic record	−20	Tuberculosis	− 1.8
1940 Joslin Clinic record	−15	Nephrectomy	− 2.0
1950 Joslin Clinic record	−10	Trace of albumin in urine..	− 5.0
		Moderate albumin in urine..	−13.5

vidual can be greatly influenced by specific genetic characters probably controlled by a single gene, as well as a complex interplay of many such characters. Metabolism plays a part in aging apparently by accelerating the appearance of the consequences of mutations.

It would be incorrect to say that any of these ideas are proven, but a strong argument can be advanced for each of them, and taken together they form a consistent picture of the biological mechanisms of senescence in the mammal.

Chapter 6

AGING IN PLANTS AND TREES

A GING in plants is certainly just as familiar a phenomenon as aging in animals, and many of the features appear almost identical in both. This has led to a widespread belief that the mechanisms of aging must also be the same for both, but it is almost certain now that such is not the case. There are probably much the same basic biological forces at work, but the interplay of these forces is quite different.

AGING IN PLANTS

As indicated in Chapter 1, an annual plant goes through a definite sequence of events from seed germination to eventual death at the end of the season, and this is all fully genetically programmed. The cessation of foliation, the flowering, setting of seed, and final withering of the plant are all controlled by genetic characters. Mutations in all these characters are known which can, within limits, change all of them. For example, a change in a single gene in clover can convert the annual variety into a biannual variety.

On the other hand, the horticulturist can alter the duration of all of these phases of plant growth by purely physiological means. The size, shape and flowering of the plant can be altered drastically by such means as available nutrient, water, light intensity, day length, etc. The length of the life span of most annual plants can be nearly doubled by picking the flower buds before they are fully formed. For example, Leopold *et al.* (1959) found that soybeans which were permitted to produce mature seeds, died at about 119 days. If the flowers were picked before formation, the plant lived for 199 days. If the seed pods were allowed to form, but removed when the seeds were very

100

immature, they lived for 161 days. It seems highly likely in this case that the formation of the seeds controls a hormone which alters the genetic program of the plant.

There is also a vast literature on the effects of various plant hormones and other chemical agents on the growth pattern of plants. Each of these causes characteristic changes and there is at least some evidence to indicate that most, if not all, the factors referred to, operate by changing the hormonal pattern of the plant.

Most plants regularly reproduce sexually by seed formation, but practically all of them can be propagated vegetatively by rooted cuttings or other means. Some species even propagate normally by this method and grasses, for example, are known to have been propagating in this way for centuries. Plants, such as *Tradescantia*, have been propagated by cuttings without change for a great many years. In each case, regardless of whether the plant was started from a seed or from a cutting, it goes through the same pattern of growth, development, and death.

Plants propagated vegetatively are then immortal in the same sense as is a culture of bacteria. As long as the plant is properly nourished it will go through its life cycle with the same somatic cell line. The cells of the plant are continually undergoing division and if a mutation occurs, which unquestionably happens, it is eliminated by cell selection. There is the possibility that a mutation may occur which confers an advantage for cell survival, or at least no disadvantage, and in this way the clonal line of the plant can change just as a culture of bacteria can change its character by mutation. This, however, is an exceedingly rare event in vegetatively propagated plants.

If the chromosomes of a somatic cell of an annual plant are examined at the end of the season (just before death) they are found to be just the same as those of a young plant. Likewise, the somatic cell chromosomes of a clone of *Tradescantia* which have been carried for many years are likewise perfect. It is then difficult to see where the mechanisms of aging discussed for animals, apply to plants. Clearly the somatic mutation theory plays no part here. The wear and tear theory seems equally untenable because a plant grown under the worst of conditions lives just as long as one grown under the best of conditions. The "rate of living" concept of a highly differentiated cell being depleted of essential RNA or proteins seems untenable for several reasons, but chiefly because the essential cells are continually undergoing division.

We then come back to the concept of the genetic program. Some biological force in both plants and animals causes differentiation of various kinds at different times. In plants it seems apparent that each new stage of differentiation produces a change in the growth pattern of the plant probably because of its influence on the hormonal pattern. The final stage creates such a serious unbalance in the growth pattern that it is no longer compatible with the life of the plant. In a very real sense, death is the final step in differentiation.

In animals, there is no doubt that the genetic program plays a major part in growth and development. Indeed in some species of fish, for example, deterioration and death follow immediately after spawning, so in this case the genetic program seems to dominate as it does in a plant. However, in most animals there is a great deal more to be considered.

AGING IN TREES

The life span of different trees varies enormously. Some live only a few years and there are some alive now which were young at the dawn of civilization (Westing, 1964). The bristlecone pines, which grow in the Sierra Nevada Mountains are the oldest known trees. The West Coast redwoods, the largest of all trees, live to be more than 3000 years of age. From this it is quite obvious that senescence in trees is not genetically programmed as it is in annual plants, although many of the patterns of growth and development in trees certainly are.

What then causes death in trees? Westing (1964), after studying the redwoods, feels they do not age in any real sense, and except for size a very young tree seems to be about the same as a very old one. The only thing that eventually causes their death is some accident such as a fire or a stroke of lightning. They are almost completely immune to disease, and even very resistant to fire.

However, there is no doubt that most trees do age and have a finite life span as do mammals. As a tree, an oak for example, gets old it ceases to grow taller, although the trunk and lower branches usually continue to grow for a long period. The reason for this is unknown, but it appears as if the sap cannot be conducted more than a certain height. When the tree is actively growing, the leaf mass increases in proportion to the tree mass, so the ability to produce the products of photosynthesis keep up with the increasing demand. As the height reaches its maximum value, the leaf area ceases to increase, thus creating a discrepancy between supply and demand, which grows steadily more unbalanced as the lower part of the tree continues to grow. In the normal tree there is a fine balance between hormone production and utilization. Since the production occurs in the leaves, as they diminish in number this balance becomes upset. Indeed an old tree has the attributes of the syndrome produced by suboptimal hormone levels.

These factors lead to a gradual deterioration of the tree. Limbs die and the trunk cannot heal itself before a fungus has become well established. The tree also seems to become more susceptible to disease. Other trees grow up around it, robbing it of nutrient and light. It is then not long before the tree is unable to cope with the problems of its environment and death soon intervenes.

It is interesting to note that there seems to be no place in this picture for the somatic mutation theory of aging, any more than there was for plants. A tree continues to grow as long as it lives. It does this by continual cell division, most of which takes place in the growing tips of the shoots known as meristems. Undoubtedly mutations occur in these cells, but, as in the dividing cells of the mammal, they continue to cleanse themselves of the mutants by cell selection. Thus a shoot taken from the top of a very old tree can be rooted to produce another identical tree. It will also be identical to the tree produced from seed. It is quite unnecessary for the tree population to "rejuvenate" itself by sexual reproduction. Some trees habitually reproduce sexually, others by clonal (vegetative) reproduction. Some employ both methods depending on the environmental circumstances. The mango, for example, produces a seed which is really a small piece of maternal tissue, stimulated to the particular shape and function by the presence of pollen. There is every evidence to indicate that clonal growth which, in a sense, is merely the continuation of one individual, can continue forever. Some clonal lines of fig trees are said to antedate the Christian era, and many fruit trees have been vegetatively reproduced for several hundred years without change.

Somatic mutations do occur in trees, but a mutation which survives to produce a changed limb, for example, is exceedingly rare. The winesap apple was such a mutation (sport) which originally occurred about 1760 and has been vegetatively reproduced ever since; but such mutations have nothing to do with aging.

It is interesting to find that a number of factors can alter the longevity of a tree. Species which live on the edge of their range, live considerably longer than their "fortunate" partners that live under near optimal conditions. Any condition which slows the growth, like a cold climate, tends to prolong the life span. Molisch (1929) made a study of plant metabolism and concluded that those plants which have a low metabolism have a long life. He pointed out that the century plant is only so named in climates where it grows very slowly and takes 100 years to produce fruit. In favorable conditions of growth it will bloom in ten years and live a correspondingly short life span. These facts are much like the conditions discussed for animals, in which a reduced metabolism will increase life span in cold blooded animals. It also revives the "rate of living" theory, but in this case apparently the increased metabolism merely serves to decrease the time until the tree gets into mechanical difficulties.

These facts then lead to the conclusion that genetically programmed senescence in trees probably plays no part in aging, nor does the production of mutations in somatic cells. The rate of living hypothesis certainly does not apply in the same way as was discussed for mammals because the cells are continually undergoing division. The concept of senescence as a consequence of the physiological unbalance between the various parts of the organism apparently plays a dominant role in such aging as occurs in trees.

AGING OF SEEDS

A seed is an embryo plant held in a state of suspended growth, and it will remain so sometimes for as long as several hundred years, as in the case of the seed of the lotus tree. Other seeds die if not germinated within a month or two. Furthermore, there is no doubt that seeds show signs of age long before they die. Plants grown from old seeds will show many more growth abnormalities than those from fresh seeds. Plants from old seeds will also exhibit many more chromosome aberrations in the growing cells and many more mutations than plants from young seeds. This was observed a number of years ago by Navaskin (1933), and has been confirmed many times since for many different kinds of seeds (see Sax, 1962).

This situation fits the concepts of the somatic mutation theory of aging perfectly. The cells of the seed exist for long periods of time without undergoing division, a condition conducive to the development of mutations and they occur in increasing numbers as the seed ages. Whether or not the developing mutations finally make the seed nonviable is not known. It would not be surprising if such were the case, nor would it be surprising if the cell metabolism were continuing on the stored RNA, and when this is exhausted the seed dies. Perhaps both mechanisms are operative in causing the aging of seeds, and one mechanism predominates in one type of seed and the other in other types.

It is interesting to note that once an old seed has germinated, it will exhibit chromosome aberrations in the meristematic cells during the first few cell divisions, but after that they are eliminated by cell selection. The plant may show a few growth abnormalities at first, but it soon grows out of them and is indistinguishable from a plant grown from a young seed. This, then, bears out the ideas discussed above that a plant will tend to throw off any spontaneous mutations which occur during its growth.

AGING IN POLLEN

It is well established that pollen ages at a much more rapid rate than seeds. The reasons for the increased rate of aging in pollen is not known, but from what is now known about aging in general, some educated guesses seem reasonable. First, pollen is composed almost entirely of DNA so there is very little RNA or proteins present to sustain the metabolism of the cell for long periods. Also, the pollen cells are haploid, so it is quite possible that recovery processes which tend to keep the somatic chromosomes stabilized, do so by virtue of the presence of the homologous chromosome. It was pointed out previously that the chromosomal repair processes require metabolic energy, and it is quite possible that the limited metabolism of the cell makes repair difficult or impossible, thus contributing to the chromosomal instability. Indeed an increased mutation rate has been observed with aging in pollen. Cartledge *et al.* (1935) kept pollen from datura at 30° C for several days and observed that the mutation rate, as judged by the rate of pollen abortion, increased many-fold. This is much like the condition with spermatozoa discussed in Chapter 5 where it was pointed out that storage of bull spermatozoa, even at low temperature for a few days, increases the mutation rate.

It appears then that aging in pollen, like that in seeds, is probably caused by a combination of mutation and deficient metabolic reserve, and it is quite possible that these factors have different importance in different pollens. This is all highly speculative at the present time, and proof will have to await further research.

BIOCHEMICAL CHANGES

In a plant, the cells all go through a period of growth and aging which is rather independent of the aging of the plant or tree. The cells in the growing point (meristem) are actively dividing and the plant increases the length of its roots and branches in this way. As the branch grows, it leaves behind the growing tip a group of cells which continue to grow by cell elongation. Gradually these cells stop elongating and become part of the woody and practically dead portion of the plant or tree. Thus by taking tissue from different parts of the plant one can get tissues with predominantly young or old cells.

When such young or old tissues are examined it is found that metabolic products, principally calcium salts, tend to accumulate in older cells (Molisch, 1929). It is possible that these products may interfere with such cell functions as membrane permeability. However, even if such could be shown to be the case, it would seem that this would have to be considered as an effect of aging rather than its cause.

When the metabolic pathways of these young and old tissues are examined, it is found that certain changes take place as the tissue ages. Gibbs and Beevers (1955) showed in pea plants that this young tissue degrades glucose almost entirely by the Embden-Meyerhof-Parnas (EMP) pathway. As the tissue grows older, however, it shifts its metabolism to the pentose phosphate pathway. Similar shifts have been reported in other tissues and in ripening fruit (Varner, 1961). The importance of these metabolic shifts is not known. However, they would be consistent with the "rate of living" theory discussed above. The enzymes or their precursors for both pathways are present when the cell undergoes the final stage of differentiation. The cells prefer the EMP degradation pathway for glucose, but when all the enzymes and corresponding RNA of this pathway are "used up," the cell must turn to the alternate pathway for its continued survival. This, again is highly speculative, but the known facts fit the general pattern.

SUMMARY

In previous chapters several possible mechanisms of aging have been discussed and it has been pointed out that probably several of them are operative, any one of which may predominate in different organisms at different times. The known data from the plant world seem to bear out this concept very well. Annual plants age according to a predetermined genetic program. Trees age by growing into mechanical difficulties or by growing into a state of physiological unbalance between the various parts of the organism so it can no longer cope with its environment. Seeds and pollen probably age by a combination of somatic mutations and "rate of living." Plants illustrate in a very striking manner the concept that there is no single mechanism of aging, but that aging is a consequence of the interplay of many factors.

reversed, and the flies were kept cold and then transferred to the warmer temperature the situation became more complex, as indicated in Figure 20. This experiment shows that aging is temperature independent for almost the first half of the life span, but becomes highly dependent on the temperature thereafter.

The situation is even more complex than this. Maynard-Smith performed an experiment in which, starting at twenty days of age, flies were kept alternately for 1 day at 30° C and for 3 days at 20° C. They survived almost as long as flies kept continuously at 20° C. They would have died in 3 days or less at any time they were transferred permanently to 30° C.

Maynard-Smith feels that the explanation of these experiments lies in the balance between production and utilization of essential cellular constituents (enzymes?). At the high temperature they are used up very rapidly. When the flies are young the produc-

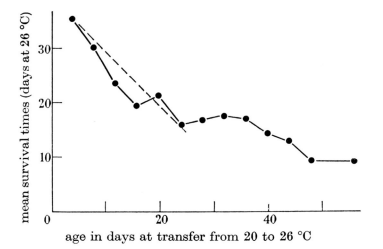

Figure 20. Mean survival times at 26° C of male *Drosophila* previously kept at 20° C for periods from four to fifty-six days. The mean survival time at 20° C was 83.4 days. If the survival were independent of temperature, the line would have a slope of −1.0 (broken line) and this is seen to be the case up to an age of about twenty-five days, after which time they age much more rapidly at the higher temperature (from Maynard-Smith, 1963).

tion can keep up with utilization even at high temperatures. As they grow older, they can no longer keep up sufficient production at high temperatures, but still can do so at low temperatures. If they are kept a short time at high temperatures, and then a period at low temperature, they can "catch up" on production and so go on about as long as they can in the cold. Eventually production cannot keep up even in the cold and this terminates life. These ideas then can be made to fit the rate of living theory in much the way Pearl visualized it.

Another important aspect of this experiment is that it tends to show that the life span of the adult *Drosophila* is not determined by mutations in the somatic cells. It would be satisfying to postulate that the animals live a shorter life span at a high temperature because mutations are produced at a higher rate at the higher temperature. However, if this were so, then the flies kept at a high temperature for the first part of their lives and a low temperature thereafter, should have developed mutations which would shorten the life span, but their life span was unchanged. It is the temperature in the latter part of the life span which is important in determining longevity, and this is just the reverse of the situation required by the mutation theory. Other evidence will be presented later to support the concept that adult *Drosophila* age by some mechanism other than mutation.

The results of experiments designed to test the effect of radiation on shortening the life span of *Drosophila* have been rather confusing. The life span of the adult can be shortened by x rays, but it takes enormous doses of the order of 50,000 rads. The concept of radiation induced aging in insects has been questioned by Strehler (1962) who found that doses as low as 5,000 rads would actually prolong the life of flies. However, Sonnenblick and Grodis (1963) repeated this work and failed to confirm it. More recently Strehler (1964) found that he was able to confirm his previous findings in some strains and not in others. Further, when flies which had their lives lengthened by the radiation were raised in a rigidly sterile condition, their lives were lengthened considerably by this procedure alone and in this case 5,000 rads of x rays had virtually no effect on the life span. It seems reasonably clear that in some cases the flies were diseased and the radiation was acting as a therapeutic agent, as it has in human medicine for many years.

Nevertheless it seems legitimate to ask why it takes 50,000 rads to shorten the life span of adult insects appreciably, and only 1 per cent of this amount to produce a comparable effect in a mammal. All the cells in the adult *Drosophila* are in the fixed post-mitotic state and highly differentiated. They are thus comparable to mammalian brain cells. As discussed in Chapter 5, the brain cells themselves are extremely resistant to radiation and it would not be at all surprising if it took doses of the order of 50,000 rads to cause an appreciable decrement of brain function. It was surmised that this is because only a small fraction of the total DNA of the cell is needed for function, so the probability of damaging an essential part is proportionately reduced. The cell never needs the rest of the DNA because it never divides. This hypothesis is certainly not proven, but it seems eminently reasonable. On this basis all the cells of the *Drosophila* are like this, and this is why they are so radiation resistant.

In defense of this position it should be pointed out that these same chromosomes are present in *Drosophila* eggs and larvae and these cells are killed by only a few hundred roentgens because of damage to the chromosomes. This gives one considerable confidence that the inherent sensitivity of insect and mammalian cells is much the same, but all post-mitotic highly differentiated cells are very radiation resistant.

It has been pointed out several times that the spontaneous mutation rate in any situation usually parallels the radiation induced mutation rate. On this basis the number of spontaneous mutations in the cells of adult *Drosophila* which affect the function of the cell must be very small indeed. It then follows that somatic mutations probably play a very small part in the aging of adult *Drosophila*. In other words, it takes a great deal of genetic damage such as is caused by doses of radiation of the order of 50,000 rads before this damage predominates as a cause of aging. Natural spontaneous mutations could not reach this level.

These conclusions are in accord with those reached recently by Clark and Rubin (1961) using the wasp *Habrobracon*. This insect produces both haploid and diploid males, which have about the same life spans. However, when the wasps are irradiated it is found that the same dose of radiation will produce a much greater shortening of the life span in the haploids than in the diploids (Fig. 21). This shows that the haploids, lacking the genetic redundancy of the diploids, are more sensitive to mutation production. When mutations dominate as the cause of death, as is the case with large doses of radiation, the haploids are shorter lived. They reason that if natural aging were due to somatic mutations, one would expect the haploid wasps to be much shorter lived than the diploids. Since they are not, natural aging must be due to some other cause. Similar results were

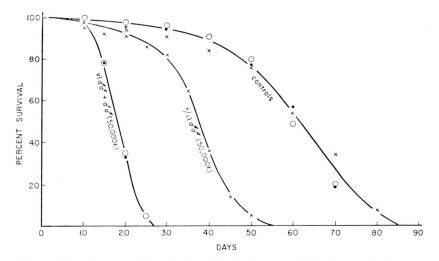

Figure 21. Life span of haploid and diploid wasps, *Habrobracon*, following a dose of 50,000 r of x rays to the young adult. Data for two different strains of haploids are presented. The open and solid circles are haploids and the crosses, diploids. This indicates a much greater radiation life shortening for haploids, but since the controls have the same life span, the conclusion is that normal life span is limited little, if at all, by somatic mutations (from Clark and Rubin, 1961).

obtained some years ago by Gowan (1931) who produced triploid *Drosophila* and showed that they did not live any longer than the diploids.

This all fits very well with the mechanisms already discussed. However, Clark and Rubin draw the further conclusion, with very good justification, that their results prove that the genetic material (DNA) of the somatic cells remains functional throughout the life of the adult. This is at variance with the conclusion reached as a result of the temperature work and it is difficult to know how to reconcile these views. The simplest explanation would be that the radiation damage is actually to the RNA rather than to the DNA, but there is no evidence to either support or deny this.

In conclusion, it seems safe to say that somatic mutations play little, if any, role in aging in adult insects, and that some form of the rate of living theory must predominate.

OTHER FORMS

Many other living creatures have been studied in a descriptive way, but these studies have little to add to our insight into the aging process. In wild animals senescence is probably a very rare or nonexistent phenomenon, so it must be studied in man or in those animals which can be kept under his protection. For most animals other than man this is quite an "unnatural" environment, so one must continually take this into account. For example, it has already been pointed out that mice and rats, when fed only about 60 per cent of what they would like to eat, may live 50 per cent longer. Is one then to consider the *ad lib* fed animals or the restricted diet ones as normal? Considerations such as these account for the fact that very little is known about the characteristics or causes of senescence in most animals.

SUMMARY

Senescence has been studied in only a very few forms of life other than mammals. The studies which have been made seem to indicate that the same basic phenomena probably hold for all forms, but their life cycles are so different from each other it is often difficult to see how the principals apply. The two most important mechanisms of senescence are the development of mutations in somatic cells and the depletion of essential constituents in post-mitotic cells. If the cells of an animal are kept in active division, either naturally or artificially, the animal can probably live indefinitely. When the cells stop dividing, however, they develop mutations or become depleted, or both, and the animal becomes senescent. It is not now possible to distinguish between these two mechanisms in most situations, but in adult insects it seems clear that mutations play no part in natural aging.

Chapter 8

CONCLUSIONS

I N THE foregoing chapters an attempt has been made to review the subject of aging from the point of view of the basic
biological mechanisms responsible for the phenomenon. From
the enormous amount of information and speculation a few facts
stand out as being of prime importance and these have led to
some tentative conclusions concerning mechanism.

First, the old question as to whether or not cells age has been
rather conclusively answered in the affirmative for the higher
forms of life, although lower forms such as single-celled
organisms can be considered immortal. If a cell differentiates
to form a specialized part of an organism, and if it does not
have the ability to revert back to the dedifferentiated state, then
its life is limited even though it may continue to undergo
division for a long time.

All the higher organisms, including man, develop from the
germ plasm by a genetically controlled program. This includes
the pattern of growth, differentiation, maturation, reproduction
and many phases of senescence.

Mutations occur in the somatic cells of the organism in large
numbers, and if the cells divide seldom, if ever, mutations
gradually increase in number until virtually every cell in some
mammalian organs has a damaged set of chromosomes. Almost
all chromosome aberrations are deleterious, so the cells become
morphologically or functionally abnormal. If the cells of an
organ are continually undergoing division, the mutations tend
to be eliminated by cell selection at the time of division, so
these organs tend to remain unaffected by age except for the
possibility of the development of a neoplasm.

When a cell undergoes differentiation and stops dividing, it

119

is endowed with a certain metabolic capacity, probably limited by the RNA present after the last division. When this RNA is all used up, the cell dies. If metabolism is forced to proceed at a faster rate, the RNA will be used up sooner. This is the modern version of the rate of living theory of aging.

These concepts seem reasonably well established and using these ideas it is possible to explain most of what is referred to as aging in both plants and animals. One or all of the various phenomena seems to be operative in the different plants or animals and in each the various causes play different parts. The primary cause of aging in one organ of an animal may be of very minor importance in another organ of the same animal.

The most important of these applications will be briefly reviewed.

1. Single-celled organisms are essentially immortal, although there is evidence that some of them must undergo a form of sexual reproduction occasionally.

2. Annual plants grow according to their genetic program, which can be varied to some extent by environmental and other conditions. The death of the plant is the last stage of the program.

3. Trees also grow according to their genetic program, but death is not part of the program. They grow by cell division and the cells seem able to continue indefinitely. The senescence and death of the tree are due to mechanical difficulties.

4. Lower forms of animal life such as insects have a genetic program with a number of stages. The final, or adult, stage is the only one in which a phenomenon that can be called aging occurs, and here the rate of living concept seems to predominate.

5. In mammals the somatic mutation concept seems of major importance. In the cells which undergo division continually like the blood cells, mutations may lead to cancer, while for the cells of other tissues, mutations may lead to the autoimmune diseases, or other forms of degeneration.

In recent years modern medicine has increased the average human life span dramatically, but the maximum life span has remained unchanged for centuries. Further, there seems to be a limit to the amount by which the death rate at any age can be decreased by modern medical methods, and most western societies are rapidly approaching this limit. If medical science is to continue its spectacular achievements in increasing the human life span, a completely new approach will be necessary.

It seems clear that this approach must involve either the prevention of the deterioration of the molecular structure of the chromosomes of somatic cells, or the development of methods for the repair of damage to DNA molecules. There are strong indications that both prevention and repair may be possible. Progress in this field will then require a much more thorough knowledge of the structure of large molecules and the forces which stabilize them.

REFERENCES

ALBERT, M. D.: X-irradiation induced mitotic abnormalities in mouse liver regenerating after carbon tetrachloride injury. I. Total body irradiation. *J. Nat. Cancer Inst., 20*:309-319, 1958.

ALEXANDER, P.: Accelerated aging—a long term effect of exposure to ionizing radiation. *Gerontologia, 1*:174-193, 1957.

ALEXANDER, P.: Do somatic mutations influence the life span of mice? In *Proc. 6th Internat. Congr. Gerontol.*, p. 26. Copenhagen, 1963.

ALEXANDER, P., and CONNELL, D. I.: Shortening of the life span of mice by irradiation with x rays and treatment with radiomimetic chemicals. *Radiation Res. 12*:38-42, 1960.

ALPATOV, W. W., and PEARL, R.: Experimental studies on the duration of life. XII. Influence of temperature during the larval and adult life on the duration of life of the imago of *Drosophila melanogaster. Am. Naturalist, 63*:37-67, 1929.

BERENBLUM, I., and TRAININ, N.: New evidence on the mechanism of radiation leukaemogenesis. In *Cellular Basis and Aetiology of Late Somatic Effects of Ionizing Radiation.* R. J. C. Harris, ed., London, Academic Press, 1963, pp. 41-52.

BERG, B. N., and SIMMS, H. S.: Nutrition and longevity in the rat. III. Food restriction beyond 800 days. *J. Nutrition, 74*:23, 1961.

BLONDAU, R. J., and YOUNG, W. C.: The effect of delayed fertilization on the development of the guinea pig ovum. *Am. J. Anatomy, 64*:303-329, 1939.

BLUMENTHAL, H. T., and BERNS, A. W.: Autoimmunity in aging. In *Advances in Gerontological Research.* B. L. Strehler, ed., New York, Academic Press, 1965, pp. 289-343.

BRENNER, S., JACOB, F., and MESSELSON, M.: An unstable intermediate carrying information from genes to ribosomes for protein synthesis. *Nature, 190*:576, 1961.

BRODY, H.: Organization of the cerebral cortex. III. A study of aging in the human cerebral cortex. *J. Comp. Neurol., 102*:511, 1955.

BUCHER, N. L. R.: Regeneration of mammalian liver. *Internat. Rev. Cytol., 15*:245-300, 1963.

BYERS, H., and MULLER, H. J.: Influence of aging at two different temperatures on the spontaneous mutation rate in mature sperma-toza of *Drosophila melanogaster. Genetics*, 37:570-571, 1952.

CALDECOTT, R. S.: Seedling height, oxygen availability, storage and temperature; their relation to radiation induced genetic injury in barley. In *Effects of Ionizing Radiations on Seeds.* IAEA, Vienna, 1961, pp. 3-24.

CARLSON, L. D., SCHEYER, W. J., and JACKSON, H. B.: The combined effects of ionizing radiation and low temperature on the metabo-lism, longevity and soft tissues of the white rat. I. Metabolism and longevity. *Radiation Res.*, 7:190-197, 1957.

CARRELL, A., and EBELING, A. H.: Age and multiplication of fibro-blasts. *J. Exper. Med.*, 35:599-623, 1921.

CARRELL, A., and EBELING, A. H.: Antagonistic growth activity and growth inhibiting principles in serum. *J. Exper. Med.*, 37:653-659, 1923.

CARTLEDGE, J. L., MURRAY, M. J., and BLAKESLEE, A. F.: Increased mutation rate from aged *Datura* pollen. *Proc. Nat. Acad. Sc. U. S.*, 21:597-600, 1935.

CHILD, C. M.: *Senescence and Rejuvinescence.* Chicago, Univ. of Chicago Press, 1915.

CLARK, A. M., and RUBIN, M. A.: The modification by x rays of the life span of haploids and diploids of the wasp, *Harbrobracon. Radia-tion Res.*, 15:244-253, 1961.

COLE, L. J., and NOWELL, P. C.: Accelerated induction of hepatomas in fast neutron irradiated mice injected with CCl_4. *Ann. N. Y. Acad. Sc.*, 114:259-265, 1964.

COMFORT, A.: *Aging, The Biology of Senescence.* New York, Holt, Rinehart and Winston, 1964.

CONKLIN, J. W., UPTON, A. C., CHRISTENBERRY, R. W., and McDONALD, T. P.: Comparative late effects of some radiomimetic agents and of x rays. *Radiation Res.*, 19:156-168, 1963.

CONNELL, D. I., and ALEXANDER, P.: The incidence of hepatomas in irradiated and nonirradiated CBA male mice as a criterion of aging. *Gerontologia*, 3:153-158, 1959.

CROWLEY, C., and CURTIS, H. J.: The development of somatic muta-tions in mice with age. *Proc. Nat. Acad. Sc. U. S.*, 49:626-628, 1963.

CURTIS, H. J.: The late effects of radiation. *Proc. Am. Phil. Soc.*, 107:5-10, 1963a.

Curtis, H. J.: Biological mechanisms underlying the aging processes. *Science, 141*:686-694, 1963b.

Curtis, H. J., and Crowley, C.: Chromosome aberrations in liver cells in relation to the somatic mutation theory of aging. *Radiation Res., 19*:337-344, 1963.

Curtis, H. J., and Gebhard, K. L.: Radiation induced aging in mice. In *Proc. 2nd Internat. Conf. on Peaceful Uses of Atomic Energy,* Vol. 22, pp. 53-57. United Nations, Geneva, 1958a.

Curtis, H. J., and Gebhard, K. L.: Comparison of life-shortening effects of toxic and radiation stresses. *Radiation Res., 9*:104, 1958b.

Curtis, H. J., and Healy, R.: Effects of radiation on aging. In *Advances in Radiobiology.* Edinburgh, Oliver and Boyd, 1957, pp. 261-265.

Curtis, H. J., Tilley, J., and Crowley, C.: The cellular differences between acute and chronic neutron and gamma ray irradiation in mice. In *Biological Effects of Neutron and Proton Irradiations,* Vol. II, pp. 143-155. IAEA, Vienna, 1964a.

Curtis, H. J., Tilley, J., and Crowley, C. The elimination of chromosome aberrations by cell division. *Radiation Res., 22*:730-734, 1964b.

Danielli, J. E., and Muggleton, A.: Some alternative states of amoeba with special reference to life span. *Gerontologia, 3*:76-90, 1959.

Das, B. C., and Bhattacharya, S. K.: Changes in human serum protein fractions with age and weight. *Canad. J. Biochem. Physiol., 39*:569-579, 1961.

Demerec, M.: Frequency of spontaneous mutations in certain stocks of *Drosophila melanogaster. Genetics, 22*:468-478, 1937.

Demerec, M.: Induced mutations and possible mechanisms of the transmission of heredity in *E. coli. Proc. Nat. Acad. Sc. U. S., 32*:36-43, 1946.

Devik, F., and Halvorsen, K.: Observations by biochemical analysis and autoradiography on labelled deoxyribonucleic acid in the normal and regenerating liver of mice. *Nature, 197*:148-150, 1963.

Dublin, L. I., Lotka, A. J., and Spiegelman, M.: *Length of Life: A Study of the Life Table.* New York, Ronald Press, 1949.

Dungay, N. S.: A study of the effects of injury upon the fertilizing power of sperm. *Biol. Bull., 25*:213-260, 1913.

FAILLA, G.: The aging process and carcinogenesis. *Ann. N. Y. Acad. Sc., 71*:1124-1135, 1958.

GIBBS, M., and BEEVERS, H.: Glucose dissimilation in the higher plant: Effect of age of tissue. *Plant Physiol., 30*:343-347, 1955.

GOWAN, J. W.: On chromosome balance as a factor in duration of life. *J. Gen. Physiol., 14*:447-461, 1931.

GOWAN, J. W.: Genetic patterns in senescence and infection. *J. Am. Geriatrics Soc., 10*:107-124, 1962.

GRAHN, D.: The genetic factor in acute and chronic radiation toxicity. In *Proc. 2nd Internat. Conf. on Peaceful Uses of Atomic Energy*, Vol. 22, pp. 394-399. United Nations, Geneva, 1958.

HARVEY, E. B.: Parthenogenetic merogony or cleavage without nuclei in *Arbacia punctulata. Biol. Bull., 71*:101-121, 1936.

HAYFLICK, L.: The limited in vitro lifetime of human diploid cell strains. *Exper. Cell Res., 37*:614-636, 1965.

HENSHAW, P. S., RILEY, E. R., and STAPLETON, G. E.: The biological effects of pile radiations. *Radiology, 49*:349-364, 1947.

HOWARD-FLANDERS, P., and BOYCE, R. P.: Release of ultraviolet light-induced thymine dimers from DNA in *E. coli. Proc. Nat. Acad. Sc. U. S., 51*:293-300, 1964.

JACOBS, P. A., BAIKE, A. G., COURT-BROWN, W. M., and STRONG, J. A.: Somatic chromosomes in mongolism. *Lancet, 1*:710, 1959.

JACOBS, P. A., COURT-BROWN, W. M., and DOLL, R.: Distribution of human chromosome counts in relation to age. *Nature, 191*:1178-1180, 1961.

JACOBSON, W.: The biology of cell division. In *Tr. 13th Conf. on Problems of Aging*, pp. 155-194. Josiah Macy, Jr., Foundation, New York, 1951.

JOHNSON, H. D., KINTNER, L. D., and KIBLER, H. H.: Effects of 48° F and 83° F on longevity and pathology of male rats. *J. Gerontol., 18*:29-36, 1961.

JONES, H. B.: A special consideration of the aging process, disease and life expectancy. In *Advances in Biological and Medical Physics*. New York, Academic Press, 1956, Vol. 4, pp. 281-336.

JONES, H. B.: The relation of human health to age, place, and time. In *Handbook of Aging and the Individual*. J. E. Birren, ed., Chicago, Univ. of Chicago Press, 1960, pp. 336-362.

JONES, D. C. L., and KIMMELDORF, D. J.: Effect of age at irradiation on life span in the male rat. *Radiation Res., 22*:106-115, 1964.

KIMBALL, R. F., GAITHER, N., and WILSON, S. M.: Recovery of stationary phase paramecia from radiation effects leading to mutation. *Proc. Nat. Acad. Sc. U. S. 45*:833, 1959.

KOHN, H. I., and GUTTMAN, P. H.: Age at exposure and the late effects of X rays. Survival and tumor incidence in CAF_1 mice irradiated at 1 to 2 years of age. *Radiation Res., 18*:348-356, 1963.

KORENCHEVSKY, V.: *Physiological and Pathological Aging.* New York, Hafner Publ. Co., 1961.

KROHN P. L.: Heterochronic transplantation in the study of aging. *Proc. Roy. Soc. London, B157*:128-147, 1963.

LANSING, A. I.: *Problems of Aging.* New York, Williams and Wilkins, 1952.

LEAVITT, R. I., and UMBARGER, H. E.: Isoleucine and valine metabolism in *E. coli.* XI. Valine inhibition of the growth of *E. coli* strain K12. *J. Bacteriol. 83*:624-630, 1962.

LEOPOLD, A. C., NEIDERGANG-KAMIEN, E., and JANICK, J.: Experimental modification of plant senescence. *Plant Physiol., 34*:570-573, 1959.

LINDOP, P. J., and ROTBLAT, J.: Long term effects of a single whole body exposure of mice to ionizing radiation. *Proc. Roy. Soc. London, B154*:332-349, 1961.

LOEB, J., and NORTHROP, J. H.: On the influence of food and temperature upon the duration of life. *J. Biol. Chem., 32*:103-121, 1917.

MAYNARD-SMITH, J.: A theory of aging. *Nature, 184*:956-957, 1959.

MAYNARD-SMITH, J.: The causes of aging. *Proc. Roy. Soc. London, B157*:115-127, 1963.

McCAY, C. M., SPERLING, L. S., and BARNES, L. L.: Growth, aging and chronic diseases and life span in the rat. *Arch. Biochem., 2*:469-477, 1943.

McGAVARCK, T. H.: Endocrine pattern during aging. *Ann. Internat. Med., 35*:961-974, 1951.

MOLISCH, H.: *Lebensdauer der Pflanze.* Jena, G. Fischer, 1929.

NAVASKIN, M.: Origin of spontaneous mutations. *Nature, 131*:439, 1933.

NEWCOMBE, H. B., and SCOTT, G. W.: Factors responsible for the delayed appearance of radiation induced mutants in *E. coli.* *Genetics, 34*:475-492, 1949.

NOVICK, A., and SZILARD, L.: Experiments with the chemostat on spontaneous mutations of bacteria. *Proc. Nat. Acad. Sc. U. S., 36*:708, 1950.

OAKBERG, E. F., and CLARK, E.: Effect of dose and dose rate on radiation damage to mouse spermatogonia and oocytes as measured by cell survival. *J. Cell. Comp. Physiol.*, 58:173-184, 1961.

PATRICK, M. H., and HAYNES, R. H.: Dark recovery phenomena in yeast. II. Conditions that modify the recovery process. *Radiation Res.*, 23:564-579, 1964.

PATRICK, M. H., HAYNES, R. H., and URETZ, R. B.: Dark recovery phenomena in yeast. I. Comparative effects with various inactivating agents. *Radiation Res.* 21:144-163, 1964.

PEARL, R.: *Studies in Human Biology.* Baltimore, Williams and Wilkins, 1924.

PEARL, R.: *The Rate of Living.* New York, A. A. Knopf, 1928.

PENROSE, L. S.: Mongolism. *Brit. Med. Bull.*, 17:184-189, 1961.

POTTER, V. R., and ONO, T.: Enzyme patterns in rat liver and Morris hepatoma 5123 during metabolic transitions. *Cold Spring Harbor Symp. Quant. Biol.*, 26:355-362, 1961.

PUCK, T. T.: Cellular aspects of irradiation and aging in animals. *Fed. Proc. Suppl. 8*, 20:31-34, 1961.

RUBNER, N.: Probleme des Wachstums und der Lebensdauer. *Mitt. Geschichte inn. Med. Wein Suppl. 9*, 7:58-81, 1908.

RUSSELL, W. L.: An augmenting effect of dose fractionation on radiation-induced mutation rate in mice. *Proc. Nat. Acad. Sc. U. S.*, 48:1724-1727, 1962.

RUSSELL, W. L.: The effect of radiation dose rate and fractionation on mutation in mice. In *Repair from Genetic Radiation*. F. Sobels, ed., New York, Pergamon Press, 1963, pp. 205-217.

SALISBURY, G. W., BRATTON, R. W., and FOOTE, R. H.: Aging of spermatozoa from cattle. *J. Dairy Sc.*, 35:256-260, 1962.

SAX, K.: Aspects of aging in plants. *Ann. Rev. Plant Physiol.*, 13:489-506, 1962.

SELYE, H.: *The Stress of Life.* New York, McGraw-Hill, 1956.

SELYE, H. and PRIORESCHI, P.: Stress theory of aging. In *Aging, Some Social and Biological Aspects*. N. W. Shock, ed., Washington, Am. Assoc. Advan. Sc., 1960, pp. 261-272.

SINEX, F. M.: Aging and lability of irreplaceable molecules. In *The Biology of Aging*. B. L. Strehler, ed., Washington, Am. Inst. Biol. Sc., 1960, pp. 268-273.

SONNEBORN, T. M.: Genetic studies on *Stenostromum incaudatum. J. Exper. Zool.*, 57:57-107, 1930.

SONNEBORN, T. M.: Enormous differences in length of life of closely related ciliates and their significance. In *The Biology of Aging.* B. L. Strehler, ed., Washington, Am. Inst. Biol. Sc., 1960, p. 289.

SONNENBLICK, B. P. and GRODIS, J.: Can a dose of 4500 r of x rays "double the longevity" of *D. melanogaster?* *Drosophila Information Serv., 37*:130, 1963.

STEFFENSEN, D.: Breakage of chromosomes in *Tradescantia* with a calcium deficiency. *Proc. Nat. Acad. Sc. U. S., 41*:155-160, 1955.

STEVENSON, K. G., and CURTIS, H. J.: Chromosomal aberrations in irradiated and nitrogen mustard treated mice. *Radiation Res., 15*:744-784, 1961.

STREHLER, B. L.: *Time, Cells, and Aging.* New York, Academic Press, 1962.

STREHLER, B. L.: Effect of X-ray dose on age-specific mortality rate in *Drosophila. J. Gerontol., 19*:83-88, 1964.

STREHLER, B. L., MARK, D., MIDVAN, A. S., and GEE, M.: Rate and magnitude of age pigment accumulation in the human myocardium. *J. Gerontol., 14*:430-439, 1959.

SULKIN, N. M., and SREVANIJ, P.: The experimental production of senile pigments in the nerve cells of young rats. *J. Gerontol., 15*:2-9, 1960.

SZILARD, L.: On the nature of the aging process. *Proc. Nat. Acad. Sc. U. S., 45*:30-42, 1959.

UPTON, A. C.: Ionizing radiation and the aging process. *J. Gerontol., 12*:306-313, 1957.

VAN'T HOF, J. and SPARROW, A. H.: The effect of mitotic cycle duraation on chromosome breakage in meristematic cells of *Pisum. Proc. Nat. Acad. Sc. U. S., 50*:855-860, 1963.

VARNER, J. E.: Biochemistry of senescence. *Ann. Rev. Plant Physiol., 12*:245-264, 1961.

VERZAR, F.: Aging of connective tissue. *Gerontologia, 1*:363-378, 1957.

WALD, N., UPTON, A. C., JENKENS, V. K., BORGES, W. H.: Radiation induced mouse leukemia: Consistent occurrence of an extra and marker chromosome. *Science, 143*:810-813, 1964.

WALFORD, R. L.: Auto-immunity and aging. *J. Gerontol., 17*:281-285, 1962.

WALFORD, R. L., and HILDEMANN, W. H.: Chronic and subacute parabiotic reactions in the Syrian hamster: significance with regard to transplantation immunity, experimental amyloidosis, and an immunologic theory of aging. *Transplantation,* 2:87-115, 1964.

WERTHESSEN, N. T.: The site of the primary lesion in atherosclerosis. *Angiology,* 13:520-530, 1962.

WESTING, A. H.: The longevity and aging of trees. *Gerontologist,* 4:10-15, 1964.

WOLF, S.: Some postirradiation phenomena that affect the induction of chromosome aberrations. *J. Cell. Comp. Physiol.,* 58:151-159, 1961.

WULFF, V. J., QUASTLER, H., and SHERMAN, F. G.: An hypothesis concerning RNA metabolism and aging. *Proc. Nat. Acad. Sc. U. S.,* 48:1373-1378, 1962.

WULFF, J. V., QUASTLER, H., SHERMAN, F. G., and SAMIS, H. V.: The effect of specific activity of H^3 cytidine on its incorporation into tissues of young and old mice. *J. Gerontol.,* 20:34-40, 1965.

ZEMAN, W., CURTIS, H. J., and BAKER, C. P.: Histopathologic effect of high energy particle microbeams on the visual cortex of the mouse brain. *Radiation Res.,* 15:496-514, 1961.

INDEX